Elementary School
Mathematics

THE LIBRARY OF EDUCATION

A Project of The Center for Applied Research in Education, Inc.

G. R. Gottschalk, Director

Categories of Coverage

I	II	III
Curriculum and Teaching	Administration, Organization, and Finance	Psychology

IV	V	VI
History, Philosophy, and Social Foundations	Professional Skills	Educational Institutions

Elementary School
Mathematics

FRANCES FLOURNOY

Associate Professor of Curriculum and Instruction
The University of Texas

The Center for Applied Research in Education, Inc.
Washington, D.C.

LIBRARY OF CONGRESS
CATALOG CARD NO.: 64–17315

PRINTED IN THE UNITED STATES OF AMERICA

Foreword

Digests of knowledge in various fields are both popular and functional. A person having a limited amount of time for reading and interested in keeping abreast of knowledge and current happenings reads a digest to serve that purpose. In the same way the teacher, principal, supervisor, and lay person may become thoroughly familiar with what is happening in the field of arithmetic by reading the monograph *Elementary School Mathematics*.

The monograph explains clearly the reason for the unprecedented changes which have taken place in arithmetic instruction within the past decade. The author emphasizes the importance of acquiring an understanding of arithmetic in order to interpret our present scientific culture. Our scientific culture has caused great changes to be made in the kind of arithmetic to be taught in today's schools.

The monograph lays great stress upon learning by discovery. Learning by this technique demands thinking with number and growth in maturity of operation with number, thus resulting in greater mathematical insight.

Chapter II deals with the structure of our number system and with the most essential properties of number which pertain to the four fundamental operations. Chapter III shows how to present these four basic operations so that the pupil will discover the principles or laws involved in performing an operation. The concise treatment of such fundamental topics in these chapters is most commendable. Teachers and others not familiar with these aspects of arithmetic will find the treatment both instructive and essential. Those who wish to broaden their understanding in this area will find the presentation helpful and stimulating.

Dr. Flournoy gives a scholarly treatment in reporting research, in dealing with investigations pertaining to modern mathematics, in compiling lists of activities for classroom usage, and in giving proper emphasis to the essential mathematical learnings which should take place in the arithmetic classroom.

FOSTER E. GROSSNICKLE

Contents

vii

Elementary School
Mathematics

CHAPTER I

Educational Objectives and the Arithmetic Curriculum

Goals of education are generally viewed in terms of the needs of the individual to be a happy, efficient, useful person in the society in which he lives. The educational program of the school attempts to develop an inquiring mind in the student and to aid him in gaining the understandings, skills, attitudes, values, and appreciations related to becoming an educated person who thinks and acts effectively and is a contributing member of society. The goals of instruction in elementary school mathematics must be balanced with the total educational program of the elementary school. A detailed description of the over-all objectives of the elementary school[1] may be consulted.

Objectives of Instruction in Arithmetic

Over the years, the objectives for teaching arithmetic in the elementary school have been both changed and broadened. They are now broadly viewed as mathematical, social, and cultural. They are interdependent and mutually supporting; each, however, needs specific attention and emphasis in a well-balanced instructional program in arithmetic. The importance of a well-balanced program in terms of social and mathematical objectives of arithmetic has been emphasized.[2]

Mathematical. The mathematical aim in the teaching of arithmetic holds that basic elementary mathematical concepts must be gained, structural features recognized, basic properties known, relationships realized, and the rationale of computation understood. When the mathematics of arithmetic is emphasized, the learner

---

[1] Nolan C. Kearney, *Elementary School Objectives* (New York: Russell Sage Foundation, 1953).

[2] B. R. Buckingham, "The Social Point of View in Arithmetic," *The Teaching of Arithmetic*, Fiftieth Yearbook, Part II, National Society for the Study of Education (Chicago: University of Chicago Press, 1951).

gains an ever-expanding understanding and insight into the structure and organization of the number system. (*Structure* refers to the study of basic principles or properties of a mathematical system.)

The school should also strive to develop in the learner a taste and inclination for the subject, flexibility in thinking, intellectual curiosity and independence, an attitude of discovery, creative but orderly thinking, the ability to make judgments, and the ability to analyze and to generalize. Whether or not the learner continues his study of mathematics in high school depends largely on the quantitative understanding, interest, and ability he gains in the elementary school. A study of junior high school pupils' attitudes toward arithmetic indicates that Grades 5 and 6 are crucial periods in the development of such attitudes.[3] A good foundation of arithmetical knowledge, understandings, skills, and attitudes is needed by all learners to continue learning mathematics in preparation for various vocations, to appreciate the role of mathematics in our cultural development, and to be effective citizens of the future.

Social. The social aim in arithmetic instruction has to do with the application of arithmetic in the interpretation and resolution of quantitative situations in daily life. Arithmetic is recognized as having usefulness and its learning becomes significant. The learner is made sensitive to numbers in social situations; he learns to use arithmetic to solve the quantitative problems of daily life and he comes to appreciate the way in which quantitative ideas are needed and used by the society in which we live.

Arithmetic should be taught because it contributes directly to effective, intelligent, and complete living: it is readily acknowledged that the learner must have a good understanding of basic mathematical ideas in order to apply arithmetic most effectively in the many and varied quantitative aspects of life. However, mathematical understanding alone does not make one efficient in the application of arithmetic to the quantitative situations of life. In order to apply mathematical understandings and skills to socially significant problems, the learner must be able to relate these concepts to quantitative social situations. It is important that a quantitative social situation be used frequently as a springboard to the introduc-

---

[3] Wilbur H. Dutton, "Attitudes of Junior High School Pupils Toward Arithmetic," *School Review,* 52 (October, 1951), 84–90.

tion of a mathematical concept. Pupils need to be guided in exploring the mathematical aspects of daily living and they must be given opportunities to use arithmetic. An important objective of arithmetic continues to be that of helping the learner develop the ability to use arithmetic to solve his quantitative problems now and in the future.

Cultural. Passing along the cultural heritage represented by great fields of knowledge has long been recognized as a function of education. The study of mathematics is part of this cultural heritage. Mathematics facilitates the development of a culture and is also shaped by that culture, as may be witnessed in the present-day development of a more modern mathematics. An appropriate knowledge of mathematics is necessary in order to appreciate the role of mathematics in our cultural development. The role that arithmetic has played in the development of culture can begin to be appreciated by the learner in the elementary school. As long as familiarity with great areas of learning remains one of the purposes of education, there is a cultural purpose for arithmetic instruction.

Historical Development of
the Arithmetic Curriculum

As the objectives of the elementary mathematics program have been changed, broadened, and clarified, parallel changes in its content and learning activities have been taking place. Consideration of the historical development of arithmetic as a school subject provides a basis from which to view the modern mathematics curriculum in the elementary school.[4]

Early records suggest that among the Babylonians and the Egyptians the arithmetic content taught was that needed in keeping records, levying taxes, telling time, surveying land, and building. The Greeks, on the other hand, were not as concerned with the practical value of arithmetic as with its theoretical nature: they taught arithmetic as the science of numbers. They studied numbers and algorisms in order to understand properties and relations. The Romans, however, were more interested in arithmetic content related directly to the practical uses of arithmetic.

Arithmetic made its entrance into the American school cur-

---

[4] Ben A. Sueltz, "Arithmetic in Historical Perspective," *The National Elementary Principal,* 39 (October, 1956), 12–16.

riculum in colonial times because it was very necessary in such fields as trade, commerce, surveying, and navigation. By the middle of the eighteenth century, arithmetic—along with reading, writing, and spelling—had become a regular part of the school curriculum. The arithmetic of this period consisted mainly of memorizing rules, classifying problems by types, and applying mechanical procedures for solving them.

During the latter half of the nineteenth century, the supposed disciplinary value of the study of arithmetic as a means of "training" the mind in memory and reasoning was emphasized. By the time the mental discipline theory was successfully challenged in the early twentieth century, the arithmetic curriculum was crowded with difficult content. A movement began to take out of the arithmetic curriculum some of the topics which were judged to be too difficult and which no longer had application in business. But along with these were abolished such mathematical topics as cube roots, repeating decimals, and formal algorisms for finding the greatest common divisor and the least common multiple. The criterion used to determine whether a topic would be kept, changed, or discarded was social utility.

During the 1920's, educational practice featured the drill approach to teaching arithmetic. Educators were concerned with identifying each element of an arithmetic process. Prior to this time, arithmetic topics such as long division were presented as a whole rather than by small steps. In the drill approach to teaching arithmetic, learning was mechanical and attention was given to identifying the steps or elements in the process rather then to understanding the arithmetical principles and relationships involved in the process as a whole.

The meaning approach was introduced in the middle 1930's. Arithmetic was described as a "system of related principles and processes."[5] By the 1940's, the need for teaching arithmetic for understanding began receiving some attention at the elementary school level. During the 1950's, the inclusion of content to give meaning and to enrich the learning of arithmetic was increasingly evidenced. Recent scientific and technological developments have put even

---

[5] William A. Brownell, "Psychological Consideration in the Learning and Teaching of Arithmetic," *The Teaching of Arithmetic*, Tenth Yearbook (Washington, D.C.: The National Council of Teachers of Mathematics, 1935).

greater emphasis on the importance of developing understanding of basic mathematical ideas in the elementary school to provide a sound foundation for continued study in the field of mathematics. Thus the mathematics curriculum is undergoing changes for improvement and modernization at all levels of instruction, from elementary school to college.

The Place of Mathematics in the Elementary School Curriculum

When arithmetic was first introduced in the elementary school curriculum during the Colonial period, it took its place in the instructional program as a separate subject. Until the 1930's there was little question regarding the place of mathematics in the elementary curriculum. During the 1930's, however, studies were made to examine the effectiveness of arithmetic learning as a part of the "activity" curriculum[6] advocated during what has been termed the "progressive education" era. The "activity" curriculum was supported by those who believed that all areas of the school program could be taught in relation to a major activity, project, or center of interest. The arithmetic achievement of pupils who followed this curriculum was found to compare favorably with that of pupils who had followed a more formal curriculum. However, it was wisely recognized by many educators that this plan would not furnish an adequate, sequential, and mathematically meaningful program. Educators generally agree that arithmetic should be taught separately in order that attention may be centered on the development of mathematical insight and understanding as well as on the application of arithmetic in the solving of socially significant problems.

Placing mathematics in the elementary curriculum as a special body of content which needs specific time and careful guidance for learning does not suggest that opportunities for relating arithmetic to other areas of the curriculum and meeting the learner's needs for handling the quantitative situations he encounters is unimportant. Whenever the teacher judges it appropriate, a situation met in another area of the curriculum may be used during the arithmetic period to provide a setting for introducing an arithmetic idea. Also,

---

6 Paul R. Hanna, "Opportunities for the Use of Arithmetic in an Activity Program," *The Teaching of Arithmetic,* Tenth Yearbook (Washington, D.C.: The National Council of Teachers of Mathematics, 1935).

there are many opportunities to apply arithmetic skills during the study of other areas of the curriculum and these should not be overlooked.

Selecting and Organizing the Content
of the Elementary Mathematics Program

Through the years, various influences—cultural, sociological, philosophical, psychological, technological and scientific—have brought about many changes in the content of the arithmetic program.

The sociological influence. The social purpose of arithmetic is concerned with the pupil's learning those arithmetic understandings and skills which are useful in his immediate and future daily life. In the early 1900's, a number of educators became concerned about the amount and kind of subject matter that was being selected from the broad field of mathematics to be taught in the elementary school. Several studies of adult usage of arithmetic indicated that only a small part of the arithmetic that was being taught in the schools at that time was needed in adult life. This concern over social usage as a basis for selecting appropriate arithmetic content reached its peak in the 1930's.

That the criterion of social usefulness has had a good effect on the arithmetic curriculum is generally accepted among educators. Social usage, however, should be considered in combination with other criteria in the selection and organization of arithmetic content to be taught in the elementary school.

The psychological influence. Principles of child development and concept formation have been considered in the determination and organization of the arithmetic curriculum. Motivation, readiness, discovery, generalization, practice, and transfer are essential elements to be considered in the organization of learning.

Although psychological studies have made some very important contributions to the field of curriculum development and learning, it is also true that they have sometimes resulted in unwise extremes. During the 1920's and early 1930's, the "connectionist" or "stimulus-response bond" theory of learning was predominant.[7] Drill on the various elements of a process was believed to fix bonds or con-

---

[7] Guy T. Buswell, "The Psychology of Learning in Relation to the Teaching of Arithmetic," *The Teaching of Arithmetic,* Fiftieth Yearbook, Part II, National Society for the Study of Education (Chicago: University of Chicago Press, 1951).

nections until automatic mastery of the entire process was achieved. Much attention was given to breaking down arithmetic topics or processes into many subskills to be presented on levels of increasing difficulty. As a result, arithmetic became too fragmented. There was too little opportunity to realize relationships.

Recent psychological studies have shown that content organized to emphasize relationships is more readily learned than content presented in an unrelated fashion.[8]

With the development of "field" learning theories, learning has been conceived of in terms of total organization rather than in terms of separate unrelated elements. Consideration of subskills by levels of difficulty will continue to play an important role in the organization of the arithmetic curriculum but must be kept in proper perspective to the whole. Arithmetic should be organized so as to emphasize underlying principles, relationships, and unifying concepts within the whole structure of mathematics.

During the 1930's, psychologists, physiologists, and sociologists were very busy acquiring data concerning child nature, growth, and development. This is frequently referred to as the "child study" movement. Studies were made of children's mental, physical, and emotional development, their rates of learning, and their interests, needs, and attitudes. Readiness as a psychological factor in learning was generally accepted. Educators became highly concerned that children should not be asked to achieve beyond their ability and that individual interests, abilities, and needs should be taken into consideration in the presentation of arithmetic topics. It was judged unwise to introduce a topic before the learner had reached a mental age high enough to profit from it. Studies were made regarding the mental age at which children seem to learn arithmetic topics most efficiently. One of these was conducted over a period of several years and in hundreds of cities by the Committee of Seven, which sought to determine the mental age at which various arithmetic topics could be taught.[9] Though this study was criticized by some

---

[8] Esther J. Swenson, "Organization and Generalization as Factors in Learning, Transfer, and Retroactive Inhibition," *Learning Theory in School Situations,* Studies in Education, No. 2 (Minneapolis, Minn.: University of Minnesota Press, 1949).

[9] C. W. Washburne, "The Grade Placement of Arithmetic Topics: A 'Committee of Seven' Investigation," *Report of the Society's Committee on Arithmetic,* Twenty-ninth Yearbook, Part II, National Society for the Study of Education (Bloomington, Ill.: Public School Publishing Company, 1930).

educators as careless and unscientific,[10] it had widespread influence on the placement of arithmetic topics. In general, the trend in curriculum organization was to move the initial presentation of certain topics to the next highest grade.

A reversal of this trend may now be noted. More recent studies have indicated that children now have a greater knowledge of arithmetic on entering school.[11] Some educators judge that with better-prepared teachers, materials, and curriculum organization, pupils can learn more arithmetic at each grade level. In view of the current interest in strengthening the mathematics program at all school levels, much attention is being centered on proposals to teach more mathematics in the elementary school.

Another psychological consideration in the organization of the content of the arithmetic curriculum is that there are various degrees of understanding in the learning of any concept or skill so that the learning of a topic is best spread over several grades rather than taught for completion within a single grade. Adherence to this principle has resulted in what is termed a "spiral" plan of organization: an arithmetic topic is begun in one grade and extended with the introduction of other and more difficult aspects of the topic in several later grades. Like any other plan, the spiral plan can also be carried to extremes. Enough time must be devoted to any new topic so that some understanding and degree of competence results. Moving too quickly from one topic to another can result in insecurity in learning.

The mathematical influence. It has long been observed that the content of the arithmetic program should be organized and presented in accordance with the sequential nature of the subject. Arithmetic, however, should not be taught as a collection of unrelated skills but as a mathematical system organized according to definite principles. The content, relationships, and unifying principles should be organized so that the logical, coherent structure of the subject is realized.

In the organization of modern mathematics programs at all levels the attempt is being made to present the basic topics of mathematics

---

[10] William A. Brownell, "A Critique of the Committee of Seven's Investigations on the Grade Placement of Arithmetic Topics," *Elementary School Journal,* 38 (March, 1938), 495–508.

[11] Angela Priore, "Achievement by Pupils Entering the First Grade," *The Arithmetic Teacher,* 4 (March, 1957), 55–60.

so that unifying ideas are stressed.[12] The unifying ideas should aid the learner to see mathematics not as a series of unrelated topics but as a systematic whole.

The inclusion of elementary content from the fields of number theory, algebra, and geometry, as well as arithmetic, points up the mathematical influence on the elementary curriculum. A well-rounded mathematics program at each grade level in the elementary school should result in a good foundation of elementary mathematical understandings.

The sociological, psychological, and mathematical bases for selecting and organizing the content of the elementary school mathematics program are interdependent. None of these criteria alone provides a sound basis for selecting and organizing arithmetic content. Balanced judgment should be used so that too much reliance is not put upon one to the neglect of the others. Careful research to establish scientifically based principles for selecting and organizing the content of the elementary mathematics program is needed.

Scope and Sequence of Topics

Since the general plan of organization of the arithmetic curriculum is a spiral plan, all the major areas of the elementary mathematics program are included at every grade level to provide a well-balanced program in each grade. These basic concepts are extended at each grade level to develop increasingly higher levels of mathematical insight. The following is an example of a scope and sequence pattern for the major areas of elementary school mathematics:

1. NUMBER AND NUMERATION

Primary grades:
Understanding 1–10 (order; one-to-one correspondence; comparing sets; cardinal and ordinal concepts);
Writing basic numerals, 0–9;
Understanding and counting the teens, 11–19;
Understanding counting by 10's, 5's, 2's, 3's, 4's;
Understanding order of counting to 100, to 1000;
Understanding base 10, place value, and additive principle to 10,000's;
Understanding meanings of 0 as no frequency in a place, not any, and a reference point;

---

[12] Frank B. Allen, *The Revolution in School Mathematics* (Washington, D.C.: The National Council of Teachers of Mathematics, 1961).

Rounding numbers to nearest ten, hundred, thousand;
Learning Roman numerals through L (50).

Intermediate grades:

Extending understanding of place value to hundred thousands, millions, and billions;

Understanding the expression of 100,000 as ($10 \times 10 \times 10 \times 10 \times 10$), 1,000,000 as ($10 \times 10 \times 10 \times 10 \times 10 \times 10$), 10,000,000 as ($10 \times 10 \times 10 \times 10 \times 10 \times 10 \times 10$), and so on;

Introduction to exponential notation, for example, 100 as 10^2, 1000 as 10^3, 10,000 as 10^4, and so on;

Rounding numbers to the nearest ten thousand, hundred thousand, million;

Learning Roman numerals to M (1000).

2. NUMBER OPERATIONS AND COMPUTATIONAL PROCEDURES WITH WHOLE NUMBERS

Primary grades:

Understanding addition and subtraction as combining and separating operations having an inverse relationship; subtraction as comparing;

Learning the order and grouping properties or principles for addition;

Understanding addition facts to sums of 10 and to sums of 18; related subtraction facts;

Solving simple equations applying addition and subtraction relationships;

Understanding addition and subtraction with two-, three-, and four-digit numerals; with and without regrouping;

Learning column addition to six‧ one-digit addends and four three- and four-digit addends;

Understanding multiplication and division as operations in combining equal sets and separating a set into smaller equal sets, and as having an inverse relationship; division as comparing;

Learning the order, grouping, and distributive properties for multiplication, and the distributive property for division;

Learning multiplication facts through sets of five or more and their reverses; related division facts;

Learning multiplication and division with two-, three-, and four-digit numerals by a one-digit multiplier and a one-digit divisor;

Solving simple equations applying multiplication and division relationships;

Understanding uneven division;

Applying skills in problem-solving.

Intermediate grades:

Extending addition and subtraction experiences with properties, facts, and computational exercises;

Learning the remainder of the basic facts of multiplication to multipliers of 9 and reverses; related division facts;

Extending multiplication and division experiences with properties and computational exercises, including two- and three-digit multipliers and divisors;

Extending experience in solving equations applying operational relationships;

Applying skills in problem-solving;

Understanding primes, composites, factors, and multiples.

3. COMMON FRACTIONS

Primary grades:

Understanding halves, thirds, fourths, sixths, and eighths of one whole;

Understanding and finding fractional parts of a group (using partition division);

Understanding simple multiple part fractions as $\frac{2}{3}$, $\frac{3}{4}$;

Comparing simple fractions and understanding simple equivalent fractions;

Understanding $\frac{2}{2}$, $\frac{3}{3}$, $\frac{4}{4}$, and so on, as names for 1.

Intermediate grades:

Extending understanding of fractional parts of a whole, as tenths, twelfths, sixteenths, and so on; finding fractional part of a group; comparing fractions and expressing equivalent fractions;

Using the terms *numerator* and *denominator;*

Understanding the concept of ratio;

Understanding and skill in adding and subtracting fractions with and without like denominators;

Understanding and skill in multiplying and dividing fractions;

Applying skills in problem-solving.

4. MEASUREMENT

Primary grades:

Understanding the concept of measurement as comparison and the meaning of standard measures;

Telling clock time and learning time relationships; understanding hour, day, week, month, year, decade, and century relationships;

Learning the common linear, liquid, dry, weight, and quantity measures and relationships;

Understanding how to read a thermometer, above and below $0°$;

Learning to change from one measure to another.

Intermediate grades:

Understanding measurement as approximation;

Extending experiences with common measures and relationships and changing from one measure to another;

Using denominate numbers;

Understanding concept of time zones in the United States and throughout the world;

Interpreting latitude and longitude;

Learning metric measures;

Understanding and finding perimeter and area of rectangular and triangular plane figures;

Understanding and finding volume of three-dimensional rectangular shapes.

5. DECIMAL FRACTIONS AND PER CENT

Primary grades:

Recognizing various coins in our system of money;

Understanding relationship of each coin to cents; of $1 to 100 cents;

Counting money to 50 cents, to $1, to $5, to $10;

Understanding equivalent amounts of money (as a dime is equivalent to two nickels, a half-dollar is equivalent to two quarters);

Making change for various amounts to $10;

Writing cents (such as 25¢); reading and writing dollars and cents (such as $1.55); reading and writing cents with dollar sign and decimal point (such as $.58);

Adding and subtracting simple amounts of money, using dollar sign and decimal point;

Multiplying and dividing simple amounts of money, using dollar sign and decimal point.

Intermediate grades:

Understanding meaning of tenths, hundredths, thousandths, ten-thousandths, hundred-thousandths;

Understanding idea of extending place to right of the ones place with each place $\frac{1}{10}$ the value of previous place;

Expressing value of each place; $\frac{1}{10}$ as $(\frac{1}{10} \times 1)$, $\frac{1}{100}$ as $(\frac{1}{10} \times \frac{1}{10})$, $\frac{1}{1000}$ as $(\frac{1}{10} \times \frac{1}{10} \times \frac{1}{10})$, $\frac{1}{10,000}$ as $(\frac{1}{10} \times \frac{1}{10} \times \frac{1}{10} \times \frac{1}{10})$;

Reading and writing decimal numerals;

Expressing decimal fractions in equivalent common fraction form; and common fractions in equivalent decimal fraction form;

Rounding decimals to nearest tenth, hundredth, thousandth;

Adding, subtracting, multiplying, and dividing decimal fractions;

Understanding concept of per cent as per hundred;

Changing per cent to decimal and common fraction forms;

Finding per cent of a number, what per cent one number is of another, and finding a number when it is expressed as a per cent of another;

Applying decimals and per cent in problems.

6. GRAPHS AND SCALE DRAWINGS

Primary grades:
  Reading and making simple picture and bar graphs;
  Understanding the idea of scale (as, one inch stands for one mile);
  Learning to read a simple scale drawing.
Intermediate grades:
  Extending experiences with reading and making picture and bar
    graphs;
  Reading and making line graphs and circle graphs;
  Making scale drawings.

7. GEOMETRIC CONCEPTS

Primary grades:
  Drawing line segments of given length with rulers;
  Learning to recognize pictures of line segment, circle, square, rec-
    tangle, triangle;
  Associating plane shapes with forms in the environment;
  Learning characteristics of rectangle; square as a special rectangle;
  Measuring length and width and writing dimensions of plane shapes in
    inches.
Intermediate grades:
  Learning the idea of an angle; learning to recognize right angles and
    right triangles;
  Understanding right triangles as half a rectangle with same dimen-
    sions;
  Recognizing triangles that are not right triangles; learning character-
    istics of equilateral triangle;
  Understanding concept of parallel lines;
  Recognizing parallelogram;
  Using term *quadrilateral* for square, rectangle, and parallelogram;
  Understanding concept of perpendicular lines;
  Learning that the distance from any point on circle to center is same,
    measuring radius and diameter of circles;
  Learning concept of three-dimensional figures as rectangular and
    triangular prisms.

Experimental Mathematics Programs

The increasing importance of science and technology in our society has focused much attention on the need to improve mathematics
education from kindergarten to college.[13] Many new and important

---

[13] *Ibid.*

uses for mathematics are being found and mathematicians and well-trained mathematics teachers are in great demand. It is being acclaimed that the school must provide a modern mathematics curriculum which will be adequate for the needs of the present and the future.

It should be noted that educators especially interested in elementary school education had already been at work to improve the elementary school arithmetic program. A movement toward teaching arithmetic for understanding and with a discovery approach began in the 1940's. These efforts and the improvements they brought about were generally unnoticed except by those most closely connected with the elementary school. Recently mathematicians have joined in the effort with professional educators and psychologists interested in curriculum development and teacher training. Financial support has been secured and proposals for improving mathematics instruction at all levels of education are receiving nationwide attention.

Since the late 1950's, a number of groups have been at work studying the content of the mathematics curriculum as well as its organization and placement and proposing changes.[14] Several foundations, such as the National Science Foundation, the Carnegie Foundation, and the Sloan Foundation, along with the U.S. Office of Education (under the National Defense Act) have provided financial support for these studies.

Some of the study groups began with efforts to design improved senior high school mathematics programs. The need to improve the junior high school program was also recognized. Then with the knowledge that the success of an improved senior high and junior high mathematics program rests on the mathematical foundation built in the elementary schools, groups began preparing proposals for changes in the elementary school mathematics program. Although proposals for rather sweeping changes in arithmetic content and grade placement are receiving increased attention, some educators warn that the program of the elementary school cannot be planned just for purposes of training future scientists and mathematicians.[15] It is asserted that the elementary school must meet the

---

[14] *Studies in Mathematics Education* (Chicago: Scott, Foresman & Company, 1960).

[15] William A. Brownell, "Principles in Curriculum Construction," *A Report of a Conference on Elementary School Mathematics* (Chicago: School Mathematics Study Group, 1959).

needs of all the pupils and that mathematics is only one of the many areas in which children must get a good foundation in the elementary school. For this reason, the mathematics program must be balanced with the total program of education in the elementary school and with the individual needs and abilities of children. A differentiated program of instruction could be one approach to meeting these individual needs.

Several of the study groups have prepared elementary mathematics teaching materials and have been experimenting with the use of these materials. In general, these experimental materials introduce certain topics in earlier grades; include some new topics; place greater emphasis on certain basic ideas, principles, and relationships of mathematics; encourage organized thinking and language; introduce more and varied experiences with equations; and provide a modern approach to the teaching of elementary geometric concepts. Some of these materials may be purchased in class quantities, but most are still in the experimental stage and further consideration and research on selection of content and grade placement is needed. And, since the programs are experimental, few are complete in terms of content, practice material, reviews, verbal problems, and tests. Content proposals being made in the experimental materials, however, will undoubtedly be used to strengthen the basic elementary mathematics program.

Information on experimental programs in elementary mathematics may be secured from the following:

School Mathematics Study Group, *Mathematics for the Elementary School,* directed by E. G. Begle. Stanford, Calif.: Stanford University, 1961.

Science Research Associates, *Elementary Mathematics Series,* directed by Bernard Gundlach. Chicago, Ill.: Originally prepared by the Educational Research Council of Greater Cleveland, 1961.

University of Illinois Arithmetic Project, directed by David A. Page. Urbana, Ill.: College of Education, University of Illinois, 1960.

The Madison Arithmetic Project, directed by Robert B. Davis. Syracuse, N.Y.: Syracuse University, 1959.

Geometry for Primary Grades, directed by Newton S. Hawley. Stanford, Calif.: Stanford University, 1961.

CHAPTER II

Basic Concepts of Elementary Mathematics

In order to guide pupils successfully in the learning of arithmetic, the teacher must possess a depth of understanding and insight into the nature and structure of elementary mathematics.[1] The elementary school teacher must stress basic mathematical ideas in the teaching of arithmetic.[2] Explanations of the structure and concepts of elementary mathematics should be carefully studied.[3]

Concept of Number

Number and numeral. Numbers are associated with sets of things. For example, the number 5 is associated with the set of fingers on one hand. The same number is associated with any set whose members can be matched one-to-one with the fingers on one hand, such as the set of players on a basketball team. Number is applied to sets of discrete objects, telling how many are in a set. Understanding of numbers develops from experience with concrete objects; however, number is an abstract concept.

Another way of representing number is in terms of points on a number line. There is a unique point on the number line which

$$0 \quad 1 \quad 2 \quad 3 \quad 4 \quad 5 \quad 6 \quad 7 \quad 8 \quad 9 \quad 10$$

corresponds to a particular number. Each number is a unique distance from 0. The point which corresponds to the number 5 is one unit further to the right of 0 than is the point which corresponds to the number 4. This concept stems from the ordinal idea of number.

---

[1] School Mathematics Study Group, directed by E. G. Begle, *Mathematics for the Elementary School: Teachers' Commentaries for Grades 4, 5, 6* (New Haven, Conn.: Yale University Press, 1960).

[2] Clifford Bell, Clela D. Hammond, and Robert B. Herrera, *Fundamentals of Arithmetic for Teachers* (New York: John Wiley & Sons, Inc., 1962).

[3] Francis J. Mueller, *Arithmetic: Its Structure and Concepts* (Englewood Cliffs, N.J.: Prentice-Hall, Inc., 1956).

Greater than is interpreted to mean *to the right of* on the number line. *Less than* is interpreted to mean *to the left of* on the number line. Every number has a successor number; therefore, every number has a predecessor. Number 5 is greater than the predecessor number, 4, but is less than the successor number, 6.

The name for a number is a symbol or a numeral that stands for the number. Mathematicians emphasize that it is important for the student of mathematics to be able to distinguish between the idea and the symbols which stand for the idea. There are many names for any number. Each of the following is a name for the same number:

$$9 \quad 7 + 2 \quad 5 + 4 \quad \text{IX} \quad 11 - 2 \quad 15 - 6$$

Just as *Jim* is a name for a boy, *9* is a name for a number. Just as it is important to distinguish between the thing (boy) and its name (Jim), so it is important to distinguish between the idea of a number and the name for the number.

Concept of sets. The teaching of the idea and the language of sets is being encouraged by some as an effective tool in expressing number ideas. A set may be thought of as a collection of things such as books, animals, cars, people, rules, numbers, points, or lines.

Each thing in a set is a member or element of the set. The members of a set may be written within braces, as the set of even numbers between 0 and 10 is: {2, 4, 6, 8}. A set can contain no members at all. For example, the set of two-digit counting numbers less than 10 has no members. Such a set is an empty set or null set and may be written { }.

Sets may be combined; this is called the union of two sets. The set of whole numbers between 1 and 15 divisible by 2 is {2, 4, 6, 8, 10, 12, 14}. The set of whole numbers between 1 and 15 divisible by 3 is {3, 6, 9, 12}. The union of these two sets is a set of numbers divisible either by 2 or by 3: {2, 3, 4, 6, 8, 9, 10, 12, 14}. In a union of two sets, all the members of both sets are included, but members appearing in both sets are listed only once.

The intersection of two sets is the set of members common to both sets. Therefore, the intersection of the two sets given above forms a set of whole numbers between 1 and 15, divisible both by 2 and by 3. This set is {6, 12}.

Cardinal and ordinal. The set of fingers on one hand, the set of toes on one foot, the set of players on a basketball team, the set of school days in a week, and any other set that can be placed in *one-to-one correspondence* with one of these sets is represented by the cardinal number 5. As a pupil works with sets of five blocks, five pencils, five pennies, five bottle tops, he gradually develops this concept of 5. In this cardinal sense, the number 5 indicates the size of the set and tells how many members the set has.

When we refer to the fifth boy in line at a water fountain, we immediately think of the four others that are ahead of this boy, for he can not be fifth unless there is a fourth, a third, a second, and a first. *Fifth* describes his position in relation to the set of four people who precede him. He is the fifth one in the cardinal 5 set. House numbers, page numbers, check numbers, telephone numbers, dates of the month and year, and the hours of the day are examples of using number in the ordinal sense. To determine the size of a set with which one is not familiar, it is necessary to count. This requires an ordering principle. A counting set possesses both cardinal and ordinal features. One counts in an increasing order, so that each number indicates the order of an object in a set, differentiates it from other members of the set, and indicates the size of the set whose members have been counted.

Natural numbers. The natural numbers are those used in counting the members of a set. The set of natural numbers begins with 1 and proceeds in an ordered sequence: 1, 2, 3, 4, ..., 97, 98, 99, 100, ... It is an infinite set.

Whole numbers. The set of natural numbers or counting numbers does not include 0; it begins with 1. The set of whole numbers does include 0. These numbers are 0, 1, 2, 3, 4, ... The 0 is used in the cardinal sense to mean "not any" and is read *zero* (as $4 - 4 = 0$).

Positive and negative integers. The need for integers arose with the need to measure from a fixed point, as on the thermometer. We speak of a temperature of 20° above 0° and mean positive 20 or $^+20$. We speak of a temperature of 20° below 0° and mean negative 20 or $^-20$.

The integers may be represented as points on a number line with 0 as a fixed reference point.

−4 −3 −2 −1 0 +1 +2 +3 +4

An integer is greater than any integer to its left (so ⁻2 is greater than ⁻4) and less than any integer to its right (so ⁻3 is less than ⁻1). In order to make all subtractions possible, such as $4 − 4 = 0$ and $3 − 4 = ⁻1$, the system of natural numbers had to be extended, so the system of numbers with which we operate includes 0 and the positive and negative integers also.

Rational numbers. A rational number is a fractional number. These are numbers that can be expressed as a/b (except when b is 0), such as ½, ¾, ⅝, ³⁄₁₀, ⁵⁄₁₂. Every whole number can be expressed in this way. For example, 2 may be expressed as ⁴⁄₂, ⁸⁄₄, ⁶⁄₃, ¹⁰⁄₅, ¹²⁄₆. The word *rational* refers to the expression of a ratio.

The denominator of a fraction indicates into how many parts a unit has been divided. The numerator indicates the number of parts counted. On the first number line below, the unit segment has been divided into two parts; on the next number line the unit segment has been divided into four parts:

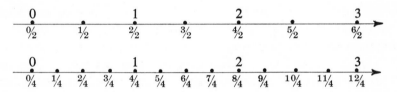

It can easily be seen that other names for 1 are ²⁄₂ and ⁴⁄₄; other names for 2 are ⁴⁄₂ and ⁸⁄₄. Another name for ½ is ²⁄₄; another name for ³⁄₂ is ⁶⁄₄.

Fractional numbers can also have decimal names, as .3 for ³⁄₁₀ and .25 for ¼. This is illustrated below:

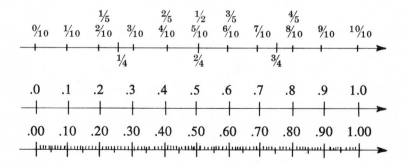

Every rational number can be expressed as a finite decimal or an infinite repeating decimal. For example, ¾ can be expressed as .75 (a finite decimal) and ⅝ can be expressed as .625. A repeating decimal expression for ⅓ is .33333 . . . , and a repeating decimal expression for ⅚ is .833333 . . . .

Natural numbers, whole numbers, positive and negative integers, and rational numbers have been discussed. The number system includes other numbers within the real number system. These, however, are beyond the scope of elementary school mathematics.

The Numeration System

A numeration system is a system for naming numbers. The symbol 5 is a name for a number.

Base ten. The decimal system of numeration is a base ten system, because it enumerates in groups of ten. The word *decimal* comes from the Latin word *decem* ("ten"). The decimal system of numeration is believed to have evolved from the fact that people have ten fingers. After matching or counting on his fingers to ten, primitive man probably thought of this as one group of that many (ten) and began again to match or count on his fingers to make another group of ten. In our decimal system we use ten basic numerals, 0, 1, 2, 3, 4, 5, 6, 7, 8, 9. The symbol 10 represents one group of ten.

Place value. The Hindu-Arabic system of numeration which we use has a base of ten and makes use of a place value principle. Every place has a value ten times as large as that of the place to its right. The place just to the left of the ones place has a value of 10 × 1, or 10. The place just to the left of the tens place has a value of 10 × 10, or 100. The next place to the left has a value of 10 × 100, or 1000.

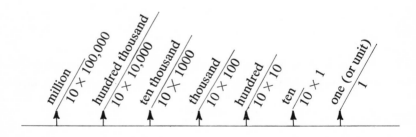

Exponential notation. Exponents are used to indicate how many times a number is to be taken as a factor. For example, we explain the value of each digit in 347 as $(3 \times 10^2) + (4 \times 10^1) + (7 \times 10^0)$, or as $(3 \times 100) + (4 \times 10) + (7 \times 1)$. The exponential form 10^3 is read *10 to the third power* and means 10 is taken as a factor three times $(10 \times 10 \times 10)$, so 10^3 means 1000. It should be understood that 10^0 means 10 is not taken as a factor any times.

In a decimal system of numeration, the following powers of 10 as assigned to each place should be understood:

$10^0 = 1$
$10^1 = (10 \times 1)$ or 10
$10^2 = (10 \times 10)$ or 100
$10^3 = (10 \times 10 \times 10)$ or 1000
$10^4 = (10 \times 10 \times 10 \times 10)$ or 10,000
$10^5 = (10 \times 10 \times 10 \times 10 \times 10)$ or 100,000
$10^6 = (10 \times 10 \times 10 \times 10 \times 10 \times 10)$ or 1,000,000
$10^7 = (10 \times 10 \times 10 \times 10 \times 10 \times 10 \times 10)$ or 10,000,000
$10^8 = (10 \times 10 \times 10 \times 10 \times 10 \times 10 \times 10 \times 10)$ or 100,000,000
$10^9 = (10 \times 10 \times 10 \times 10 \times 10 \times 10 \times 10 \times 10 \times 10)$
$\qquad\qquad$ or 1,000,000,000

The value of each place in a numeral may be expressed as below:

10^4	10^3	10^2	10^1	10^0
6	6	6	6	6

It is important to note that the power of 10 in each position corresponds to the number of places to the left of the ones place.

Extending the numeration system to the right. It is important to understand that in going to the right in a decimal place value system of numeration, each place has $\frac{1}{10}$ the value of the previous place. The 4 in ④ 4 4.44 has a value $\frac{1}{10}$ as great as the ④ because 40 is $\frac{1}{10}$ of 400. The 4 ones has $\frac{1}{10}$ the value of the 4 tens because 4 is $\frac{1}{10}$ of 40. The 4 tenths has $\frac{1}{10}$ the value of 4 ones. Continuing to the right, 4 hundredths is $\frac{1}{10}$ the value of 4 tenths. The chart below shows how we extend the idea of place value to the right of the units place. It should be carefully noted that the units place is the center or pivot from which to count places to the left or the right in the numeration system.

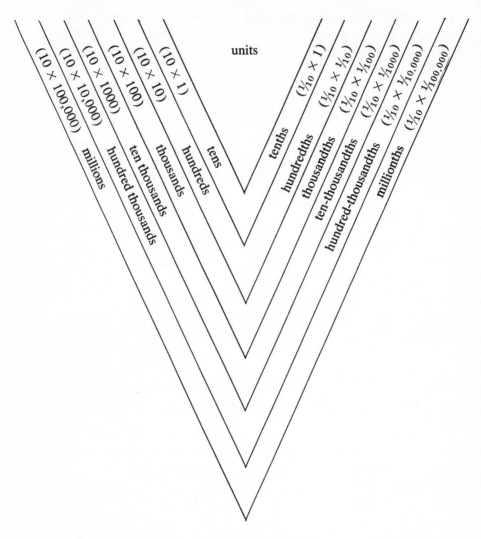

The powers of 10 as assigned to each place to the right of the decimal point should be understood as follows:

$$\tfrac{1}{10}{}^1 = (\tfrac{1}{10} \times 1) \text{ or } \tfrac{1}{10}$$
$$\tfrac{1}{10}{}^2 = (\tfrac{1}{10} \times \tfrac{1}{10}) \text{ or } \tfrac{1}{100}$$
$$\tfrac{1}{10}{}^3 = (\tfrac{1}{10} \times \tfrac{1}{10} \times \tfrac{1}{10}) \text{ or } \tfrac{1}{1000}$$
$$\tfrac{1}{10}{}^4 = (\tfrac{1}{10} \times \tfrac{1}{10} \times \tfrac{1}{10} \times \tfrac{1}{10}) \text{ or } \tfrac{1}{10,000}$$
$$\tfrac{1}{10}{}^5 = (\tfrac{1}{10} \times \tfrac{1}{10} \times \tfrac{1}{10} \times \tfrac{1}{10} \times \tfrac{1}{10}) \text{ or } \tfrac{1}{100,000}$$
$$\tfrac{1}{10}{}^6 = (\tfrac{1}{10} \times \tfrac{1}{10} \times \tfrac{1}{10} \times \tfrac{1}{10} \times \tfrac{1}{10} \times \tfrac{1}{10}) \text{ or } \tfrac{1}{1,000,000}$$

It is important to note that the power of $\frac{1}{10}$ as assigned to each place in a decimal numeral corresponds to the number of places to the right of the ones place.

10^0	$\frac{1}{10}^1$	$\frac{1}{10}^2$	$\frac{1}{10}^3$	$\frac{1}{10}^4$	$\frac{1}{10}^5$	$\frac{1}{10}^6$
2	.2	2	2	2	2	2

Other number bases. In understanding base and place value in a numeration system, it is important to realize that any whole number (except 1 and 0) could be used as a base. Of course, base ten is characteristic of a decimal system of numeration. Base five is a quinary system, base eight is an octonary system, and base twelve is a duodecimal system. Base two, a binary system is used in electronic computers.

In a numeration system using the place value principle, the base of the system determines the number of basic numerals that are used in writing numerals in that system. In our base ten system, ten basic numerals are used. These are 0, 1, 2, 3, 4, 5, 6, 7, 8, 9. In a base five system, only five basic numerals would be used: 0, 1, 2, 3, 4. In a base eight system, eight basic numerals would be used: 0, 1, 2, 3, 4, 5, 6, 7. Base two, a binary system, uses 0, 1.

Regardless of the base, the symbol for one group of the base in a place value plan can always be 10. In a base ten system this symbol means one ten. In a base five system, five will also be written 10 and will mean one five.

In a base five system, the counting numbers are expressed in order as 1, 2, 3, 4, 10, 11, 12, 13, 14, 20. Since the symbol 10 means *five* in this system, the symbol for 1 five and 1 one is 11. This symbol in base five is best read as *1 five and 1* rather than as *eleven,* because *eleven* is the term used in a base ten system to mean *1 ten and 1*. In base five the symbol 12 means 1 five and 2 ones and is best read as *1 five and 2*. The symbol 13 in a base five system means 1 five and 3 ones and should be read *1 five and 3* rather than as *thirteen,* which is only a base ten term meaning *ten and 3*. After the symbol 14, the sequence of counting numbers goes to two groups of five, because there is no other basic numeral after 4 to be used with one group of five in a base five system. The symbol 20 in base five means 2 fives and 0 ones. The symbol 24 in base five means 2 fives and 4 ones and has a value of nineteen in base ten. The following are grouped by fives and the numerals are in base five.

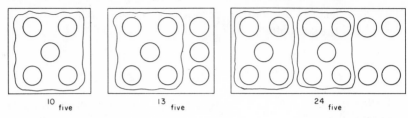

Continuing with base five the symbols after 20 are 21, 22, 23, 24, 30, 31, 32, 33, 34, 40, 41, 42, 43, 44, 100. The symbol 44 means 4 fives and 4 ones and has a value of twenty-four in base ten. In base ten the symbol 100 means 10^2 or 10×10. In base five the symbol 100 means 5^2 or 5×5 and has a value of twenty-five.

In base five the numerals after the symbol 100 follow in order as 101, 102, 103, 104, 110, 111, 112, 113, 114, 120, 121, 122, 123, 124, 130, 131, 132, 133, 134, 140, 141, 142, 143, 144, 200. After the symbol 444, meaning $(4 \times 5^2) + (4 \times 5^1) + (4 \times 1)$, the next symbol is 1000, which means 5^3 or $5 \times 5 \times 5$. In base ten, the symbol 1000 means 10^3 or $10 \times 10 \times 10$.

In base ten the numeral 432 means $(4 \times 10^2) + (3 \times 10^1) + (2 \times 10^0)$ or $(4 \times 100) + (3 \times 10) + (2 \times 1)$ or $400 + 30 + 2$. To determine in base ten the value of the base five symbol 432, the base ten symbol 5 will be used for the symbol 10 (which means one five in base five. Therefore, in base five the numeral 432 means $(4 \times 5^2) + (3 \times 5^1) + (2 \times 5^0)$ or $(4 \times 25) + (3 \times 5) + (2 \times 1)$. This equals $100 + 15 + 2$, or 117, in base ten.

Nonpositional numeration systems. It is the positional or place value characteristic of the Hindu-Arabic numeration system which makes it a very efficient system. The Roman numeral system was not a place value system in the same sense. DCCCLXXIII is the Roman numeral for 873. It can be noted that the value of C does not change with its position, as CCC means $100 + 100 + 100$. Likewise, the value of X is ten and the value of I is 1, regardless of their position.

Another interesting nonpositional system was the Egyptian system. The following symbols were used:

| $=$ 1 (uplifted finger) $\int$ $=$ 10,000 (bent reed)

∩ $=$ 10 (heelbone or arch)   ∝ $=$ 100,000 (polliwog)

$\mathcal{G}$ = 100 (coil of rope) $\mathcal{X}$ = 1,000,000 (astonished man)

$\mathcal{Y}$ = 1000 (lotus flower)

The Egyptian symbol $\mathcal{((99999 \cap |||||}$ would mean 20,416. It is obvious that the value of a symbol did not change with its position: $\mathcal{((}$ would mean 10,000 + 10,000 and $\mathcal{9999}$ would mean 100 + 100 + 100 + 100.

Number Operations

The four basic number operations are addition, subtraction, multiplication, and division. Addition and multiplication involve putting sets or groups together. Subtraction and division involve separating sets or groups. Multiplication is sometimes viewed as being related to repeated addition of equal sets or groups, as $4 + 4 + 4 = 12$, so $3 \times 4 = 12$. Division is sometimes viewed as being related to repeated or serial subtraction of equal sets or groups, as $12 - 4 = 8$; $8 - 4 = 4$; $4 - 4 = 0$ (three 4's have been subtracted) so the answer to $12 \div 4$ (how many 4's equal 12?) is 3. This subtractive idea relates to division when division is used in the measurement sense. When division is used in the partitive sense, 12 divided by $4 = ?$, the size of each part is being found, so a subtractive relationship is not involved in the same way.

Each number operation should also be viewed as a mathematical operation with certain properties or characteristics. When operating on whole numbers, addition and multiplication are always possible and the result is always another whole number, as $5 + 9 = 14$ and $3 \times 7 = 21$. Sometimes the operations of subtraction and division on two whole numbers produce another whole number, as $12 - 4 = 8$ and $15 \div 3 = 5$. However, this is not always true for subtraction and division of whole numbers: $4 - 7$ and $3 \div 5$ do not produce whole number results.

Addition and subtraction. Inverse operations "undo" each other. If 4 is added to 8, the addition may be "undone" by subtracting 4 from the results. The end result is the same as the number with which we began, as $8 + 4 = 12$; $12 - 4 = 8$. If 4 is subtracted from 12, the subtraction may be "undone" by adding 4 to the result, as $12 - 4 = 8$; $8 + 4 = 12$.

In addition we add two known addends to find a sum. In subtraction we subtract a known addend from a known sum to find the other addend. The following illustrates this relationship:

Multiplication and division. These are inverse operations. For example, 3 × 5 = 15 may be "undone" by dividing the results by 5, as 3 × 5 = 15; 15 ÷ 5 = 3. The end result is the same as the number with which we began. If 15 is divided by 5, the division may be "undone" by taking the results times 5, as 15 ÷ 5 = 3; 3 × 5 = 15.

In multiplication we multiply two known factors to find a product. In division we divide a known product by one known factor to find the other factor. The following illustrates this relationship:

Identity elements. Zero is the identity element for addition; for example, 8 + 0 = 8 and 0 + 8 = 8. The addition of 0 to any number always yields the number to which it is added; the addition of any number to 0 always yields the number added. Zero is also the identity element for subtraction when 0 is being subtracted, as 6 − 0 = 6.

The identity element for multiplication is 1; for example, 1 × 7 = 7 and 7 × 1 = 7. The multiplication of any number by 1 always yields the number being multiplied; the multiplication of 1 by any number always yields the number by which 1 is being multiplied. The identity element for division is also 1 when a number is being divided by 1, as $9 \div 1 = 9$.

Mathematical Relationships
of Equality and Inequality

The symbol for equality is $=$. A mathematical sentence, such as $7 + 8 = 15$, expresses an equality relationship. It is read, *7 plus 8 equals 15*. This means that "$7 + 8$" and "15" are names for the same number.

The symbol for inequality is $\neq$. A mathematical sentence may express inequality as $3 \times 7 \neq 24$. This means that "3×7" and "24" are not names for the same number. The statement is read, *3 times 7 is not equal to 24*.

The symbol used to express the relationship *greater than* is $>$, as in the mathematical sentence, $9 > 3$. This is read, *9 is greater than 3*. The symbol used to express the relationship *less than* is $<$, as in the mathematical sentence, $12 < 15$. This is read, *12 is less than 15*.

Some mathematical sentences are true, as $2 + 8 = 10; 9 - 4 = 5; 7 > 3; 8 < 12$. Others are false, as $3 \times 5 = 16; 14 \div 7 = 3; 9 < 7; 16 > 20$. Still other mathematical sentences are "open" sentences because there is an unknown, as $9 - n = 6$. If n is 3, the sentence will be $9 - 3 = 6$, which is true. If n is 4, the sentence will be $9 - 4 = 6$, which is false. If n is 4, then $24 \div n = 6$ is a true sentence. If n is 8, then $4 \times n = 36$ is a false sentence.

Properties of Number System

Commutative property for addition. The order of two addends may be changed without changing the results: $3 + 4 = 7$, $4 + 3 = 7$; and $3 + 4 = 4 + 3$. In general, if $a + b = c$, then $b + a = c$; or $a + b = b + a$. This is the commutative property, law, or principle for addition. It is sometimes referred to as the "order" property for addition. That is, we can "commute" or reverse the order in which two numbers are added without affecting the sum.

Commutative property for multiplication. The order of two factors may be changed without changing the results: $5 \times 7 = 35$, $7 \times 5 = 35$; and $5 \times 7 = 7 \times 5$. In general, if $a \times b = c$, then

$b \times a = c;$ or $a \times b = b \times a$. This is the commutative or "order" property, law, or principle for multiplication. That is, we can "commute" or reverse the order of two factors being multiplied without affecting the product.

Associative property for addition. In the addition with three or more addends, the addends may be grouped in different ways without changing the results: $(5 + 3) + 7 = 15; 5 + (3 + 7) = 15;$ and $(5 + 3) + 7 = 5 + (3 + 7)$. In general, if $(a + b) + c = d$, then $a + (b + c) = d$. This is the associative property for addition; it is sometimes referred to as the "grouping" property for addition. The word *associate* suggests that, when adding with three numbers, we may associate either the first pair or the second pair. The association intended is usually shown by parentheses. When numerals are enclosed within parentheses, the operation indicated within is performed first.

In studying basic facts of addition, this principle may be applied conveniently, as $8 + 7 = (5 + 3) + 7 = 5 + (3 + 7)$. The association of $5 + (3 + 7)$ makes the easy addition of $5 + 10$, or 15. Of course, other groupings or associations can also be made as $(6 + 2) + 7 = 6 + (2 + 7)$.

Associative property for multiplication. In multiplication with three or more factors, the factors may be grouped in different ways without changing the results: $(6 \times 2) \times 4 = 48, 6 \times (2 \times 4) = 48;$ and $(6 \times 2) \times 4 = 6 \times (2 \times 4)$. In general, if $(a \times b) \times c = d$, then $a \times (b \times c) = d;$ or $(a \times b) \times c = a \times (b \times c)$. In studying basic facts of multiplication, this principle may be applied conveniently as $6 \times 4 = (3 \times 2) \times 4 = 3 \times (2 \times 4) = 3 \times 8 = 24$.

Distributive property for multiplication with respect to addition. When two or more addends are to be multiplied by the same number, the sum of the addends may be multiplied by the number, or the products of the factors may be added, as $9 \times (2 + 4) = (9 \times 2) + (9 \times 4) = 18 + 36 = 54$. This distribution was to the right. In general, this principle may be stated as $a \times (b + c) = (a \times b) + (a \times c)$. Distribution to the left may be used also, as $(4 + 5) \times 6 = (4 \times 6) + (5 \times 6) = 24 + 30 = 54$. In general this may be stated as $(a + b) \times c = (a \times c) + (b \times c)$.

Distributive property for division with respect to addition. When two or more addends are to be divided by the same number, the sum of the addends may be divided by the number, or the quotients may be added, as $(42 + 6) \div 6 = (42 \div 6) + (6 \div 6) = 7 + 1 = 8$. Division is distributive only to the left. In general, this is stated as $(a + b) \div c = (a \div c) + (b \div c)$.

Primes, Composites, Factors, and Multiples

An understanding of prime numbers, composite numbers, factors, and multiples is basic to the finding of a greatest common factor and a least common multiple. In operating with fractions, these procedures most commonly are referred to as *finding the greatest common divisor* (for changing fractions to "simplest form") and *finding the least common denominator* (for adding and subtracting unlike fractions).

Prime numbers. A prime number is a counting number greater than 1 that has no counting number factor other than 1 and itself. A factor is a number by which any other number can be divided without a remainder. The set of prime numbers less than 10 is $\{2, 3, 5, 7\}$. The only factors of 2 are 1 and 2; the only factors of 3 are 1 and 3; the only factors of 5 are 1 and 5; the only factors of 7 are 1 and 7; therefore, 2, 3, 5, and 7 are prime numbers. The number 1 is not usually included as a prime number or as a composite number; every number whether prime or composite has 1 as a factor.

Composite numbers. A composite number is a counting number greater than 1 that has factors other than 1 and itself. The set of composite numbers less than 10 is $\{4, 6, 8, 9\}$. The counting number factors of 4 are 1, 2, 4; the counting number factors of 6 are 1, 2, 3, 6; the counting number factors of 8 are $\{1, 2, 4, 8\}$ and the counting number factors of 9 are $\{1, 3, 9\}$.

Testing for primeness. To test a number for primeness, it is necessary to test only those prime factors whose squares are the same or less than the number being tested. For example, is 87 a prime number? The largest prime number whose square is the same or less than 87 is 9. The primes less than 9 are 7, 5, 3, 2. We may divide 87 by each of these and find that 87 is divisible by 3 without a remainder. Therefore, 87 has factors of 1, 3, and 87. It is not a prime number; it is a composite number.

Expressing numbers as products of primes. Every number

greater than 1 is either a prime number or may be expressed as a product of primes. The steps in expressing 30 and 48 as products of primes are shown below:

$30 = 6 \times 5$ (6 is a composite and may be expressed as 2×3)

$\quad = (2 \times 3) \times 5$

$48 = 6 \times 8$ (both 6 and 8 are composites)

$\quad = (2 \times 3) \times 8$ (2 and 3 are primes)

$\quad = (2 \times 3) \times (2 \times 4)$ (4 is a composite number)

$\quad = (2 \times 3) \times (2 \times 2 \times 2)$ (all factors are now primes).

Finding all the factors of a number. To find all the factors of a number, the number can first be expressed as a product of primes, as $48 = 2 \times 3 \times 2 \times 2 \times 2$. By then multiplying these factors in pairs, other factors of 48 can be found as shown below:

$$48 = 2 \times 3 \times 2 \times 2 \times 2$$

By multiplying 2×3 and 2×2, it is seen that 6 and 4 are also factors (not prime factors) of 48. By multiplying in groups of three, other factors may be found as shown below:

$$48 = 2 \times 3 \times 2 \times 2 \times 2$$

It can be seen since $2 \times 3 \times 2 = 12$ and $2 \times 2 \times 2 = 8$, that 12 and 8 are also factors of 48. By multiplying in groups of four, it can be seen that $2 \times 3 \times 2 \times 2 = 24$, which is another factor of 48. It is not necessary to go further because the multiplication of all five factors when expressed as a product of primes is already known to be 48, but of course both 48 and 1 are factors of 48. All the factors of 48 have then been found to be 1, 2, 3, 4, 6, 8, 12, 24, and 48.

Common factors and greatest common factor. The greatest common factor for two numbers is the greatest number by which both can be divided evenly. The greatest common factor of 6 and 9 is 3, that of 8 and 12 is 4, and that of 16 and 24 is 8. By trial division of the greater number by each of the factors of the other number (beginning with the greatest factor), the greatest common factor can be discovered. Since the greatest common factor of 16 and 24 is 8, then $^{16}\!/_{24}$ may be changed to simplest form by dividing the numerator and denominator by 8.

To determine the greatest common factor for 24 and 42, each of the numbers may first be expressed as products of primes.

$$24 = (2 \times 3) \times (2 \times 2)$$
$$42 = (2 \times 3) \times 7$$

By looking for those primes that appear in both products, the greatest common factor may be found. It can be seen that 2×3 appears in both factors so 2×3 or 6 is the greatest common factor of 24 and 42.

In a similar way the greatest common factor for 84 and 116 can be found:

$$84 = 6 \times 14 \quad \text{or} \quad (2 \times 3) \times (2 \times 7)$$
$$116 = 4 \times 28 \quad \text{or} \quad (2 \times 2) \times (7 \times 2 \times 2)$$

The common prime factors can be grouped together as:

$$84 = 2 \times 3 \times (7 \times 2)$$
$$116 = 2 \times 2 \times 2 \times (7 \times 2)$$

The greatest common factor of 84 and 116 is 7×2 or 14.

Multiples and least common multiple. The multiples of a number are the numbers which have the given number as a factor. For example, the multiples of 6 are 6, 12, 24, 30, 36, 42, ... There is, of course, no greatest multiple for any number. The multiples of 6 or of any number is an infinite set.

The least common multiple of two numbers is the smallest number which has each of the two given numbers as factors. The least common multiple of 2 and 5 is 10; that of 3 and 6 is 6; and that of 4 and 6 is 12. To find the least common multiple of two numbers such as 24 and 40, each of the numbers may first be expressed as a product of primes as shown:

$$24 = 3 \times 2 \times 2 \times 2$$
$$40 = 2 \times 2 \times 2 \times 5$$

The least common multiple of 24 and 40 must have both 24 and 40 as factors. When the least common multiple is expressed as a product of primes it must contain both of the above sets of factors as shown below:

$$24 = 3 \times 2 \times 2 \times 2$$
$$24 \text{ and } 40 = 3 \times 2 \times 2 \times 2 \times 5$$
$$40 = 2 \times 2 \times 2 \times 5$$

Therefore, $3 \times 2 \times 2 \times 2 \times 5$, or 120, is the least common multiple of 24 and 40.

The least common denominator can frequently be determined by inspection as for $\frac{1}{2} + \frac{3}{5}$; $\frac{2}{3} + \frac{1}{6}$; and $\frac{3}{4} + \frac{1}{6}$, or by application of a simple procedure of multiplying the largest denominator by 2, by 3, and so on until a least common denominator is found as for $5\frac{5}{9} + 6\frac{7}{12}$. However, it would not be easy to use either of these two methods to find the least common denominator for $8\frac{9}{14} + 5\frac{7}{16}$, so the method of first expressing each number as a product of primes would simplify the process of finding a least common denominator. The least common multiple includes only those factors needed so that both 14 and 16 are factors of it, as shown:

$$14 = 7 \times 2$$

$$16 = 2 \times 2 \times 2 \times 2$$

$$
\begin{array}{c}
\overbrace{}^{14} \\
\text{L.C.M. of 14 and 16} = \quad 7 \times 2 \times 2 \times 2 \times 2 = 112 \\
\underbrace{}_{16}
\end{array}
$$

Since the least common multiple for 14 and 16 is 112, then the least common denominator for $8\frac{9}{14} + 5\frac{7}{16}$ is 112.

Computational Rationale

An understanding of the underlying mathematical principles is essential in the learning of every arithmetical procedure. The learning of a topic involves knowing *why* as well as *how* a certain procedure is used. There are important understandings to be gained regarding addition, subtraction, multiplication, and division with whole numbers, fractions, and decimals.

The rationale of computation with whole numbers. The addition of whole numbers is based on the associative principle. The use of such procedures is of great value in helping the learner to understand addition of whole numbers, as in the example:

$\begin{array}{r} 34 \\ +\ 52 \\ \hline 86 \end{array}$	$\begin{array}{r} 3 \text{ tens } 4 \text{ ones} \\ +\ 5 \text{ tens } 2 \text{ ones} \\ \hline 8 \text{ tens } 6 \text{ ones} \end{array}$	$\begin{array}{r} 30 + 4 \\ +\ 50 + 2 \\ \hline 80 + 6 = 86 \end{array}$

The use of the associative principle as an essential part of the computational procedure is shown in the example:

$$34 + 52 = (30 + 4) + (50 + 2)$$
$$= (30 + 50) + (4 + 2)$$
$$= 80 + 6$$
$$= 86$$

The use of sticks or other devices in bundles of tens and ones is, of course, recommended for the understanding of the "carrying" which may be necessary in addition. The learner understands "carrying" as a regrouping procedure. The use of varied number methods to illustrate this principle is considered of much value in understanding "carrying" or regrouping, as in the example:

①

48	4 tens 8 ones	40 + 8
+ 26	+ 2 tens 6 ones	+ 20 + 6
74	6 tens 14 ones	60 + 14 = 14
	= 6 tens + (10 ones + 4 ones)	+ 60
	= (6 tens + 1 ten) + 4 ones	74
	= 7 tens 4 ones	
	= 74	

In each method it can be noted that 10 ones have been regrouped as 1 ten and added to 6 tens to make 7 tens. Each of these methods is a simple use of the associative principle. A more formal way of illustrating the use of the associative principle for this addition is shown below:

$$48 + 26 = (40 + 8) + (20 + 6)$$
$$= (40 + 20) + (8 + 6)$$
$$= 60 + 14$$
$$= (60 + 10) + 4$$
$$= 74$$

Again, the use of bundles of sticks or other devices is recommended for developing an understanding of "borrowing" or regrouping in subtraction. A twenty-bead abacus may also be used. However, meaningful number methods should be used as an intermediate stage between the use of concrete materials and the computational procedure to be learned as for the example:

$$\begin{array}{r} 6\ 14 \\ \not{7}\not{4} \\ -\ 26 \\ \hline 48 \end{array}$$

7 tens 4 ones	6 tens 14 ones	$70 + 4$	$60 + 14$
or		or	
$-$ 2 tens 6 ones	$-$ 2 tens 6 ones	$- 20 + 6$	$- 20 +\ \ 6$
	4 tens 8 ones		$40 +\ \ 8 = 48$

Addition involves finding the sum of two given addends. Subtraction involves finding an addend when a sum and one addend are given. An understanding of the inverse relationship between addition and subtraction is basic to solving simple equations as the following:

$$\begin{aligned} 26 + n &= 84 \\ n &= 84 - 26 \\ n &= 58 \end{aligned}$$

Principle: A sum (84) and one addend (26) are given. To find unknown addend (n), subtract.

$$\begin{aligned} n + 215 &= 432 \\ n &= 432 - 215 \\ n &= 217 \end{aligned}$$

Principle: A sum (432) and one addend (215) are given. To find unknown addend (n), subtract.

$$\begin{aligned} n - 65 &= 92 \\ n &= 92 + 65 \\ n &= 157 \end{aligned}$$

Principle: Two addends (92 and 65) are given. To find unknown sum (n), add.

$$\begin{aligned} 436 - n &= 128 \\ n &= 436 - 128 \\ n &= 208 \end{aligned}$$

Principle: A sum (436) and one addend (128) are given. To find unknown addend (n), subtract.

The algorism or computational procedure used in the multiplication of whole numbers is based on the distributive principle for multiplication with respect to addition. The use of varied number methods is of great value for aiding the learner in understanding multiplication of whole numbers, as in the example:

③
  38
× 4
───
152

3 tens 8 ones
×   4
12 tens 32 ones
= 12 tens + (30 ones + 2 ones)
= (12 tens + 3 tens) + 2 ones
= 15 tens 2 ones = 152

30 + 8	120
× 4	+ 32
120 + 32	152

In each method it can be noted that 30 ones have been regrouped as 3 tens and added to 12 tens to make 15 tens. Each of the methods is a use of the distributive principle in a simple way. A more formal way of illustrating the use of the distributive principle for this multiplication is shown below:

$$4 \times 38 = 4 \times (30 + 8) = (4 \times 30) + (4 \times 8) = 120 + 32 = 152$$

The application of the distributive principle in multiplying by a two-digit number may also be understood by using varied number methods, as the two methods shown below for the example:

  37
× 26
───
222
 74
───
962

37	37	222
× 20	× 6	+ 740
740	222	962

37
× 26
222
740
962

It can be noted that multiplying 37 by 20 or 2 tens yields 740 or 74 tens. The use of the procedure of placing a 0 in the ones position as shown is recommended in the beginning. Later the shorter method shown (without the 0) may be used. The application of the distributive principle may be also noted as below:

$$\begin{aligned} 26 \times 37 &= (20 + 6) \times 37 \\ &= (20 \times 37) + (6 \times 37) \\ &= 740 + 222 \\ &= 962 \end{aligned}$$

The algorism or computational procedure used in the division of whole numbers is based on the distributive principle for division with respect to addition. The use of varied number methods is of great value for aiding the learner in understanding division of whole numbers, as shown below for the example:

$$
\begin{array}{r}
52 \\
3\overline{)156} \\
15 \\
\hline
6 \\
6 \\
\hline
\end{array}
$$

5 tens 2 ones = 52
$3\overline{)\ 15 \text{ tens } 6 \text{ ones}}$

$50 + 2$
$3\overline{)\ 150 + 6}$

$$
\begin{array}{r}
52 \\
2 \\
50 \\
3\overline{)156} \\
150 \\
\hline
6 \\
6 \\
\hline
\end{array}
$$

It can be noted that 15 tens or 150 ones are divided by 3 and then the remaining 6 ones are divided by 3. The use of a procedure to encourage showing a 0 in the ones place of the first multiplication step (as on the right above) is recommended in the beginning. Later the shorter method (without the 0) should be used ("bring down" actually means subtract). The application of the distributive principle may be also noted as below:

$$
\begin{aligned}
156 \div 3 &= (150 + 6) \div 3 \\
&= (150 \div 3) + (6 \div 3) \\
&= 50 + 2 \\
&= 52
\end{aligned}
$$

Multiplication is finding a product when two factors are given. Division is finding a factor when a product and one factor are given. An understanding of the inverse relationship between multiplication and division is basic to solving simple equations as the following:

$8 \times n = 296$
$n = 296 \div 8$
$n = 37$

Principle: A product (296) and one factor (8) are given. To find unknown factor (n), divide.

$n \times 43 = 602$
$n = 602 \div 43$
$n = 14$

Principle: A product (602) and one factor (43) are given. To find unknown factor (n), divide.

$n \div 26 = 7$
$n = 7 \times 26$
$n = 182$

Principle: Two factors (7 and 26) are given. To find unknown product (n), multiply.

$$144 \div n = 16$$
$$n = 144 \div 16$$
$$n = 9$$

Principle: A product (144) and a factor (16) are given. To find unknown factor (*n*), divide.

The rationale of computation with fractions. Through the use of fractional parts, pictures, and an improvised method, the principle of adding or subtracting the numerators of fractions and keeping the same denominator is developed:

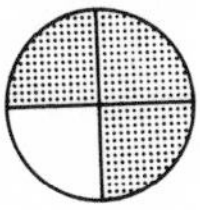

$$\begin{array}{r} 3 \text{ fourths} \\ + \ 1 \text{ fourth} \\ \hline 4 \text{ fourths} = 1 \end{array}$$

$$\tfrac{3}{4} + \tfrac{1}{4} = \tfrac{4}{4} = 1$$

The need to arrive at fractions with like denominators in order to add or subtract may be developed through efforts to find the answer without having like denominators:

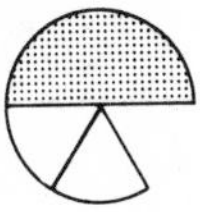

$$\begin{array}{r} 1 \text{ half} \\ + \ 2 \text{ thirds} \\ \hline ? \end{array}$$

$$\tfrac{1}{2} + \tfrac{1}{3} = ?$$

Other names for these fractions, with like denominators, may be found by using a fraction chart:

1					
½			½		
⅓		⅓		⅓	
⅙	⅙	⅙	⅙	⅙	⅙

It can be seen that ½ and ³⁄₆ are names for the same fraction, and ⅓ and ²⁄₆ are names for the same fraction. By using ³⁄₆ for ½ and ²⁄₆ for ⅓, the principle used in adding like fractions may then be applied:

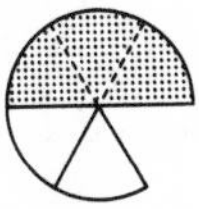

1 half	or	3 sixths
+ 1 third	or	2 sixths
		5 sixths

$$\tfrac{1}{2} + \tfrac{1}{3} = \tfrac{3}{6} + \tfrac{2}{6} = \tfrac{5}{6}$$

By studying the fractional chart it can also be noted that when halves are expressed as sixths, the number of parts in the whole is three times greater (since $6 = 3 \times 2$) and the number of parts in each one-half of a whole is three times greater. With sufficient experiences in noting that there are many names for the same fraction ($\frac{1}{2}$, $\frac{2}{4}$, $\frac{3}{6}$, $\frac{4}{8}$, $\frac{5}{10}$ are all names for the same fraction and $\frac{1}{3}$, $\frac{2}{6}$, $\frac{3}{9}$, $\frac{4}{12}$, $\frac{5}{15}$ are all names for the same fraction), a generalization may be derived. To express an equivalent fraction with higher terms, as $\frac{1}{3} = \frac{4}{12}$, the numerator and denominator may be multiplied by the same number. Through meaningful experiences, it may also be generalized that to express an equivalent fraction with lower terms, as $\frac{4}{12} = \frac{1}{3}$, the numerator and denominator may be divided by the same number.

The associative principle for addition is basic to the procedure used in the addition of whole and fractional numbers, as $4\frac{1}{8} + 2\frac{3}{8} = (4 + \frac{1}{8}) + (2 + \frac{3}{8}) = (4 + 2) + (\frac{1}{8} + \frac{3}{8}) = 6 + \frac{4}{8} = 6\frac{1}{2}$. In the addition of fractional numbers the answer is usually changed to simplest form, as $1\frac{5}{8} + 2\frac{1}{2} = 1\frac{5}{8} + 2\frac{4}{8} = 3\frac{9}{8} = 4\frac{1}{8}$. The use of fractional parts helps to gain the meaning of the expression, $3\frac{9}{8} = 4\frac{1}{8}$.

The use of fractional parts as shown below aids in understanding "borrowing" or regrouping as needed in this subtraction example:

$$3\frac{1}{4} = 2\frac{5}{4}$$
$$- 1\frac{3}{4} = 1\frac{3}{4}$$
$$\overline{\phantom{-1\frac{3}{4} = }1\frac{2}{4} = 1\frac{1}{2}}$$

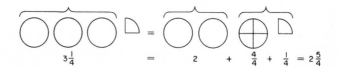

The relationship of an integer times a fraction and the addition of equal addends may be illustrated on a number line as shown for $6 \times \frac{2}{3}$.

It can be noted that six ⅔'s = 4. Using addition of equal addends 6 × ⅔ is expressed as ⅔ + ⅔ + ⅔ + ⅔ + ⅔ + ⅔ = ¹²⁄₃ = 4. From this experience it may be concluded that the numerator of the fraction may be multiplied by the whole number and placed over the denominator, as 6 × ⅔ = ¹²⁄₃ = 4. That 4 is a name for ¹²⁄₃ is illustrated on the number line below:

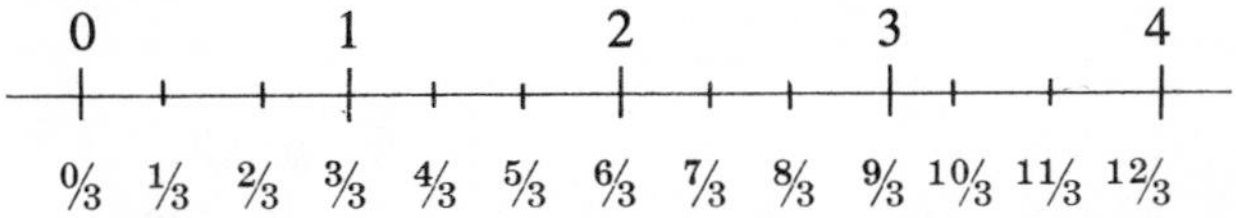

```
   0         1         2         3         4
 --+--+--+--+--+--+--+--+--+--+--+--+--
  0/3 1/3 2/3 3/3 4/3 5/3 6/3 7/3 8/3 9/3 10/3 11/3 12/3
```

How many groups of 3 thirds are in 12 thirds may be noted as 4. This is the same as how many 3's are in 12.

It can also be noted on the number line that ⁷⁄₃ and 2⅓ are names for the same number. The number of 3 thirds in 7 thirds is seen to be 2⅓. Another name for ⁶⁄₃ is 2; another name for ⁸⁄₃ is 2⅔.

The principle of expressing a fraction, such as ⁹⁄₄, as the fractional number, 2¼, may be illustrated using fractional parts to find how many 4 fourths are in 9 fourths. In 9 fourths there are "two and one-fourth" 4 fourths. It may be discovered that the number of 4 fourths in 9 fourths may be found by dividing the numerator (9) by the denominator (4), as 9 ÷ 4 = 2¼. It may then be generalized that an improper fraction can be expressed as a whole and fractional

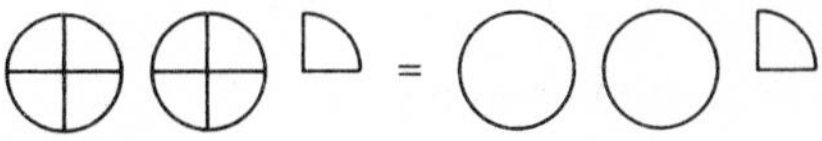

⊕ ⊕ ◺ = ○ ○ ◺

⁹⁄₄　　or　　(⁴⁄₄ + ⁴⁄₄ + ¼)　　=　　2¼

number by dividing the numerator of the fraction by the denominator.

The multiplication of a fraction by an integer may be rationalized as illustrated for ⅔ × 9.

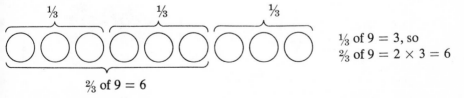

⅓ of 9 = 3, so
⅔ of 9 = 2 × 3 = 6

⅔ of 9 = 6

This thinking is an application of the associative principle for multiplication, as ⅔ × 9 = (2 × ⅓) × 9 = 2 × (⅓ × 9) = 2 × 3 = 6.

The more usual procedure for finding the product of $\frac{2}{3} \times 9$ may be examined through the use of the following illustrations:

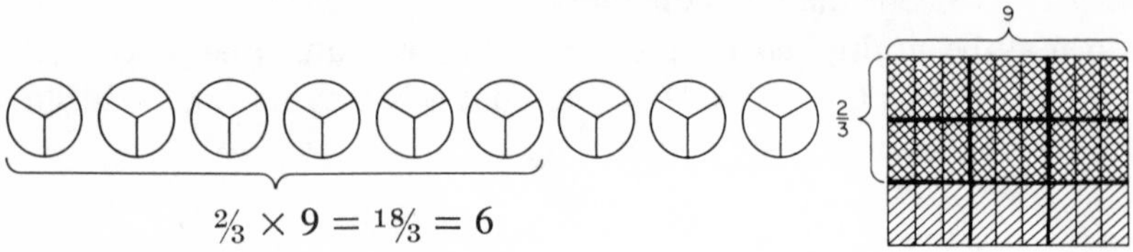

$\frac{2}{3} \times 9 = \frac{18}{3} = 6$

In the illustration on the left, the fact that the product is $\frac{18}{3}$ or 6 is clearly discernible. In the rectangular illustration, the 18 thirds are regrouped to show 6 groups of thirds. It may be concluded that the product of a fraction and a whole number may be found by multiplying the numerator and the whole number and then dividing this product by the denominator.

To find the product of a whole number and a mixed number, the distributive principle may be applied, as $3 \times 2\frac{2}{3} = (3 \times 2) + (3 \times \frac{2}{3}) = 6 + 2 = 8$. If the procedure of multiplying is as $3 \times \frac{8}{3}$, the understanding of expressing $2\frac{2}{3}$ as $\frac{8}{3}$ is needed as shown. It may be generalized that the whole number times the denominator (2×3)

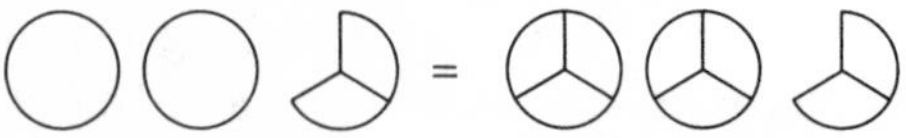

2 $\frac{2}{3}$ $= (2 \times \frac{3}{3}) + \frac{2}{3}$ or $(\frac{6}{3} + \frac{2}{3}) = \frac{8}{3}$

plus the numerator (2) of the fraction $(6 + 2)$ or (8), divided by the denominator (3) may be used to yield the fraction $\frac{8}{3}$, because this is a short-cut way of changing the whole number to an equivalent fraction, $\frac{6}{3}$, and adding $\frac{2}{3}$ to make $\frac{8}{3}$.

The meaning of a fraction times a fraction, as $\frac{1}{2} \times \frac{2}{3}$, may be illustrated in the following ways:

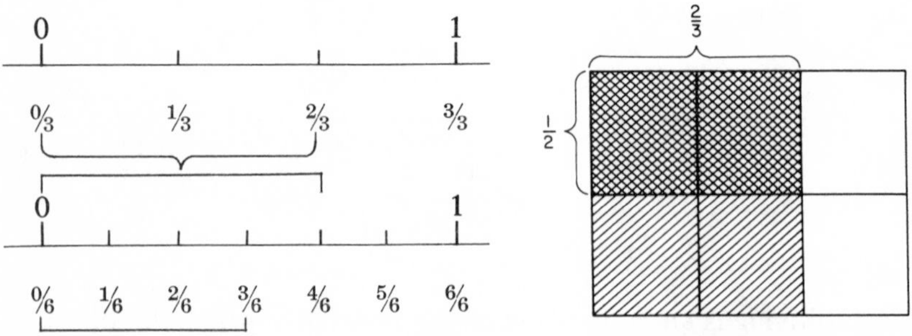

$\frac{1}{2}$ of $\frac{2}{3} = \frac{2}{6}$ or $\frac{1}{3}$

$\frac{1}{2} \times \frac{2}{3} = \frac{2}{6} = \frac{1}{3}$

It may be concluded that multiplying the numerators gives the number of parts involved, and multiplying the denominators yields the size of the parts.

To rationalize the division of a whole number by a fraction, as $4 \div \frac{2}{3}$, it might most meaningfully be read, "how many two-thirds equal 4?" A number line procedure and a related subtractive method are shown below:

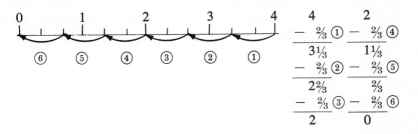

It can be seen that beginning at 4 and counting the number of two-thirds back to 0 yields 6 two-thirds. The same idea is illustrated with the serial subtraction of two-thirds.

A common denominator division method of finding "how many two-thirds equal 4" may be explained also by studying the number line illustration. It can be noted that in 4 there are 12 thirds, so $\frac{12}{3}$ is a name for 4. It may then be concluded that $4 \div 2$ thirds $= 12$ thirds $\div 2$ thirds $= 6$. The common denominator algorism for division of 4 by $\frac{2}{3}$ is

$$4 \div \frac{2}{3} = \frac{12}{3} \div \frac{2}{3} = \frac{6}{1} = 6$$

Rationalizing the "invert and multiply" procedure is more difficult. By studying a unit section of the number line divided into thirds, it may be noted that there are $1\frac{1}{2}$ two-thirds in one:

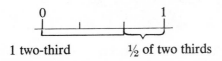

1 two-third $\frac{1}{2}$ of two thirds

Therefore, since there are $1\frac{1}{2}$ two-thirds in one unit, there are $4 \times 1\frac{1}{2}$ two-thirds in four units. To use the "invert and multiply" method, the procedure is $4 \div \frac{2}{3} = (4 \times 1\frac{1}{2}) = 4 \times \frac{3}{2} = \frac{12}{2} = 6$. The inverted form of the divisor may be explained as the number of parts, the size of the divisor, that are found in one unit. To find how many of that size in several units, multiply by the number of units.

Another explanation of the "invert and multiply" algorism for dividing with fractions is the reciprocal explanation. Every number except 0 has an inverse which is referred to as its reciprocal. The reciprocal of 2 is $\frac{1}{2}$; that of 4 is $\frac{1}{4}$; that of $\frac{2}{3}$ is $\frac{3}{2}$. The reciprocal of a number is a number it can be multiplied by and yield 1. Another principle involved in the reciprocal explanation is that if the same number is multiplied by each term of a fraction, the value of the fraction does not change, as $\frac{2}{3} \times \frac{2}{2} = \frac{4}{6}$. Using these two principles the reciprocal explanation for the division of 4 by $\frac{2}{3}$ is:

$$\frac{4}{\frac{2}{3}} = \frac{4 \times \frac{3}{2}}{\frac{2}{3} \times \frac{3}{2}} = \frac{4 \times \frac{3}{2}}{1} = 4 \times \frac{3}{2} = \frac{12}{2} = 6$$

In another form this idea appears as:

$$\begin{aligned} 4 \div \tfrac{2}{3} &= (4 \times \tfrac{3}{2}) \div (\tfrac{2}{3} \times \tfrac{3}{2}) \\ &= (4 \times \tfrac{3}{2}) \div 1 \\ &= 4 \times \tfrac{3}{2} = \tfrac{12}{2} = 6 \end{aligned}$$

Therefore, we may shorten the method, as $4 \div \frac{2}{3} = 4 \times \frac{3}{2} = \frac{12}{2} = 6$.

Dividing a fraction by a whole number, as $\frac{2}{3} \div 4$, means that we are trying to find the size of one of four equal parts of two-thirds. This may be illustrated as below:

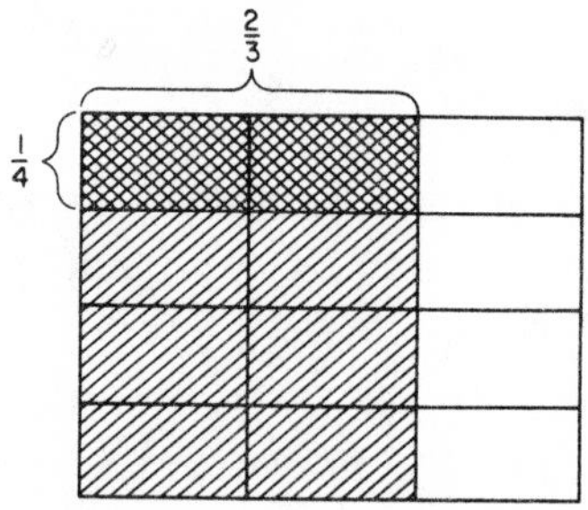

$$\tfrac{2}{3} \div 4 = \tfrac{1}{4} \text{ of } \tfrac{2}{3} = \tfrac{2}{12} = \tfrac{1}{6}$$

Since $\frac{2}{3} \div 4$ means $\frac{1}{4}$ of $\frac{2}{3}$, using the commutative principle, this may be expressed as $\frac{2}{3} \times \frac{1}{4}$. Applying the "invert and multiply" or the reciprocal principle, the common algorism is $\frac{2}{3} \div 4 = \frac{2}{3} \times \frac{1}{4} = \frac{2}{12} = \frac{1}{6}$.

The rationale of computation with decimals. The principles regarding place value and the addition and subtraction of common fractions are basic to understanding addition and subtraction of decimal fractions as shown:

$5\frac{3}{10}$	5 ones 3 tenths	5.3
$+\ 3\frac{4}{10}$	$+$ 3 ones 4 tenths	$+$ 3.4
$8\frac{7}{10}$	8 ones 7 tenths	8.7

The use of visual aids and varied number methods help to illustrate the meaning of regrouping or "carrying" and "borrowing" in addition with decimals:

Step A		Step B		Step C	
Ones	tenths	Ones	tenths	Ones	tenths
I I I I	I I I I I I I				
I I	I I I I I I	I I I I I I	(I I I I I I I I I) I I	I I I I I I ⓪	I I I
$3\frac{7}{10}\ +\ 2\frac{6}{10}$	$=$	$5\frac{13}{100}$	$=$	$6\frac{3}{10}$	

4 ones   7 tenths
$+$ 2 ones   6 tenths
6 ones 13 tenths
$=$ 7 ones   3 tenths

It can be noted that the "carried" one means that 10 tenths have been regrouped as 1. The meaning of "carrying" or regrouping from hundredths to tenths may be understood by means of similar procedures:

Step A					
ones	tenths	hundredths	1 one 2 tenths 4 hundredths		
I	I I	I I I I	$+$ 2 ones 3 tenths 7 hundredths		
I I	I I I	I I I I I I	3 ones 5 tenths 11 hundredths		
			$=$ 3 ones 6 tenths 1 hundredth		

Step B		
I I I	I I I I I	(I I I I I I I I I I) I

Step C		
I I I	I I I I I ⓪	I

①
1.24
$+$ 2.37
3.61

It can be noted that 11 hundredths are regrouped as 10 hundredths and 1 hundredth. The value of $^{10}\!/_{100}$ is $\frac{1}{10}$ so .1 is "carried."

The meaning of regrouping or "borrowing" in subtraction with decimals may be developed in a similar manner:

		12	14	
	6 ones	$\not{3}$ tenths	$\not{4}$ hundredths	
−	3 ones	9 tenths	7 hundredths	
	2 ones	3 tenths	7 hundredths	

$$\begin{array}{r} {\scriptstyle 5\ 12\ 14} \\ \not{6}.\not{3}\not{4} \\ -\ 3.97 \\ \hline 2.37 \end{array}$$

It is shown that 1 tenth has been regrouped as 10 hundredths ($\frac{1}{10}$ = $^{10}\!/_{100}$), and added to 4 hundredths to make 14 hundredths; 1 one has been regrouped as 10 tenths and added to the 2 tenths left to make 12 tenths.

From experiences with visual aids and varied number methods, it is concluded that when adding and subtracting tenths, the answer is in tenths; when adding and subtracting hundredths, the answer is in hundredths. To add and subtract tenths and hundredths, tenths are expressed as hundredths just as with fractions:

$$\begin{array}{r} 5\ ^{6}\!/_{10} = 5^{60}\!/_{100} \\ +\ 2^{27}\!/_{100} = 2^{27}\!/_{100} \\ \hline 7^{87}\!/_{100} \end{array} \qquad \begin{array}{r} 5.6\ = 5.60 \\ +\ 2.27 = 2.27 \\ \hline 7.87 \end{array}$$

To find the answer to 3×2.3, several number methods may be used:

$$\begin{array}{r} 2.3 \\ 2.3 \\ 2.3 \\ \hline 6.9 \end{array}$$

$$\begin{aligned} 3 \times 2^{3}\!/_{10} &= 3 \times {}^{23}\!/_{10} \\ &= {}^{69}\!/_{10} \\ &= 6^{9}\!/_{10} \end{aligned}$$

2 ones	3 tenths
×	3
6 ones	9 tenths

$$\begin{array}{r} 2.3 \\ \times\ 3 \\ \hline 6.9 \end{array}$$

It is then noted that a whole number times tenths yields tenths. In an example such as 2.3×3.7, a fraction method aids in understanding the placement of the decimal point in the answer:

$$2^{3}\!/_{10} \times 3^{7}\!/_{10} = {}^{23}\!/_{10} \times {}^{37}\!/_{10} = {}^{851}\!/_{100} = 8^{51}\!/_{100}$$

It may be noted that tenths times tenths equals hundredths which is indicated by two decimal places to the right of the ones place as shown in the product, 8.51.

$$
\begin{array}{r}
3.7 \\
\times\ 2.3 \\
\hline
111 \\
74 \\
\hline
8.51
\end{array}
$$

With fractions the placement of the decimal point in the product of 2.3×1.43 may be understood as:

$$2\tfrac{3}{10} \times 1\tfrac{43}{100} = \tfrac{23}{10} \times \tfrac{143}{100} = \tfrac{3289}{1000} = 3\tfrac{289}{1000}$$

The fact that tenths times hundredths equals thousandths is indicated by three decimal places to the right of the ones place as shown in the product, 3.289.

$$
\begin{array}{r}
1.43 \\
\times\ \ 2.3 \\
\hline
429 \\
286 \\
\hline
3.289
\end{array}
$$

To determine the number of decimal places in a product, the number of decimal places to the right of the ones place in the numbers being multiplied may be counted or added. This is a quick way of multiplying denominators which are powers of 10.

To understand the procedure for dividing a decimal fraction by a whole number, as $6.9 \div 3$, the use of place value devices and varied number methods is helpful:

Step A		Step B			
ones	tenths	ones	tenths	2 ones	3 tenths
IIIIII	IIIIIIIII	II	III	3)6 ones	9 tenths
		II	III		2.3
		II	III		3)6.9
					6
					9
$6\tfrac{9}{10} \div 3 = 6\tfrac{9}{10} \times \tfrac{1}{3} = 6\tfrac{9}{30} = 2\tfrac{3}{10}$					9

Tenths divided by a whole number yields tenths, or one decimal place to the right of the ones place (as in 2.3). In a similar way, it can be shown that hundredths divided by a whole number yields hundredths, so $4.68 \div 2 = 2.34$. It may be concluded then that when dividing a decimal fraction by a whole number, the number of decimal places in the answer is the same as the number of decimal places in the number being divided.

Division by a decimal fraction is a more difficult procedure. To rationalize the division, $.4 \overline{)2}$, a number line may be used as shown below:

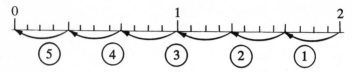

By counting the number of 4 tenths in 2 (or 20 tenths), it can be seen that there are five. The common denominator method of dividing fractions may be used to represent the number line procedure:

$$2 \div \tfrac{4}{10} = {}^{20}\!/_{10} \div \tfrac{4}{10} = {}^{20}\!/_{4} = 20$$

It can be rationalized that an equivalent expression for $.4 \overline{)2}$ is $4 \overline{)20}$. A shorter procedure for expressing $.4 \overline{)2}$ as $4 \overline{)20}$ is that of multiplying 10 by the divisor and the dividend. This is the same principle as that which is used to express any fraction in higher terms:

$$\frac{2 \times 10}{.4 \times 10} = \frac{20}{4} = 5 \qquad\qquad .4 \overline{)2} = 4 \overline{)20}^{\;5}$$

A quicker procedure is to multiply as shown but to use a caret or arrow for the new decimal place in the divisor and the dividend as:

$$.4 \overline{)2.0_{\wedge}}^{\;5.}$$

By use of this procedure the divisor may always be changed to a whole number when multiplied by the appropriate power of 10. The dividend is multiplied by the same power of 10. In the example $.15 \overline{)\,.45}$, 100 is the appropriate power of 10 for expressing the divisor as a whole number, so the divisor and dividend may be multiplied by 100:

$$.15 \overline{)\,.45}^{\;3} = 15 \overline{)45}^{\;3} \qquad .15 \overline{)\,.45_{\wedge}}^{\;3.}$$

The subtractive method is sometimes applied for placing the decimal point in the answer when dividing by a decimal fraction. This method can be rationalized as shown for $4.54 \div .2$:

$$454\%_{100} \div \%_{10} = {}^{454}\!\%_{100} \div \%_{10}$$
$$= {}^{454}\!\%_{100} \times {}^{10}\!\%_{2}$$
$$= {}^{4540}\!\%_{200}$$
$$= 22\%_{10}$$

It can be noted that hundredths divided by tenths yields tenths in the answer. To determine the number of decimal places in the quotient, the number of decimal places (1) in the divisor may be subtracted from the number of decimal places (2) in the dividend:

$$
\begin{array}{r}
22.7 \\
.2\,\overline{)4.54} \\
4 \\
\hline
5 \\
4 \\
\hline
14 \\
\end{array}
$$

This indicates one decimal place in the answer for this example. This procedure is the inverse of the additive plan used in multiplication of decimal fractions. This is a quick way of dividing denominators which are powers of 10.

Measurement

Measuring is a comparing process. It is a matter of selecting a unit of measure and comparing it to the thing to be measured to see how many of the units are contained in it.

Concrete familiar things within primitive man's environment became referents in comparing or measuring. Some of the ancient measures were: (a) girth: distance around the body; (b) cubit: from elbow to tip of middle finger; (c) span: from end of thumb to tip of little finger; (d) palm: breadth of four fingers side by side; (e) ell: from middle of chest, or the nose, to tip of thumb of one outstretched arm; (f) fathom: distance between tips of thumbs with both arms outstretched; (g) foot: length of one foot; (h) pace: distance from heel of one foot to heel of the next foot when placed in walking position; (i) furlong ("furrow-long"): length of furrow to be plowed before stopping to let the oxen rest; (j) acre: amount of land that could be plowed in one morning; and (k) stone's weight, arrow's flight, day's journey, handful, or gourdful.

Man gradually realized a need for more uniform measures so that the beginnings of some of the standard measures of today were the foot stick, the cubit stick, the ell stick, and the fathom stick, which many ancient people used.

The English system of measures, which is commonly used in the United States today, was derived from such early measures as described above. As trading and industry increased in Colonial times, the need for standard units of length, weight, and liquid and dry measure became crucial. Units of measure are now carefully defined by law.

The metric system of measures was established in the eighteenth century in France and is based on the decimal system of notation.

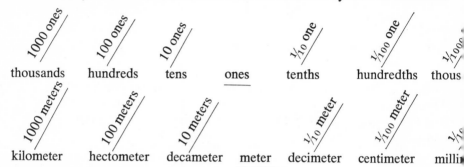

| thousands | hundreds | tens | ones | tenths | hundredths | thous |

| kilometer | hectometer | decameter | meter | decimeter | centimeter | milli |

It is the official system of measures in many countries and is used consistently by scientists of the world, because it permits much more accurate measurement. Even in the United States, the standard for linear measurement is the meter. The yard, which is a little less than a meter, is defined as $\frac{3600}{3937}$ meter. The inch, foot, and mile, as well as the centimeter and millimeter, are officially defined in terms of the meter. Models and records for this and all other standard measures are kept in the United States Bureau of Standards.

It should be understood that measurement is always approximate. With careful application of very refined measuring devices, any measurement can be made to a greater degree of precision. However, some degree of error is present in any measurement. The situation in which a measurement is being taken determines the degree of precision needed. The pharmacist who fills a prescription must measure to a greater degree of precision than does the grocer who is weighing apples.

Finding the perimeter of a rectangle, triangle, parallelogram, or any polygon has to do with "measuring around" or finding the total length of the line segments which form the figure. Finding the area means determining the size of a surface or plane region which has the two dimensions of length and width. The unit of measure is a two-dimensional unit. Area may be thought of as the number of such units which it would take to cover the interior or plane region. Finding the volume means measuring the capacity or solid region of a three-dimensional figure having length, width, and height. The unit of measure is a three-dimensional unit. Finding the volume of a rectangular prism may be thought of as finding the number of three-dimensional units, or cubes, needed to fill its interior.

Elementary Geometry

The word *geometry* was derived from two Greek terms meaning "earth measurement." Traditionally, geometry has dealt with the properties and measurement of lines, angles, plane surfaces, and solids. Geometry has recently been defined as a study of space and location.

It is now being recommended that the elementary school mathematics program should include the development of some simple geometric concepts. There are representations of geometric ideas in the things we see in the world around us. It is judged that elementary school children can effectively develop some of these basic geometric ideas intuitively. The representations of geometric ideas on paper are, of course, just pictures of the ideas; therefore, it is well to speak of such representations as, for example, a *picture* of a line segment, a *picture* of a circle, or a *picture* of an angle. Some basic geometric ideas are presented briefly here.

Point. A point is an exact location that has no size and cannot be seen or felt. The point of a pin or the point where two streets intersect are representations of a point. A point is a fixed location. If a pin is held in a certain position, its tip represents a geometric point in space. If the pin is moved, its tip now represents a different geometric point, but the point originally represented by the pin point would remain fixed or unchanged.

Space. Space is defined as the set of all points or possible locations in the universe.

Path. A path contains more points than could ever be counted. A curve drawn on paper is a picture of a path. A trail through the woods and a city street are representations of paths in the world around us.

Line segment. A line segment is the most direct path between two endpoints. A straight path drawn with a ruler and a pencil to connect two points is a picture of a line segment. A stretched string is a model of a line segment.

Line. A line is the extension of a line segment in both directions. It is necessary to use one's imagination to think of this extension as continuing on and on without end.

Plane. Through a line in space there are an infinite number of planes. A table top, a floor, or any flat surface is a physical representation of a plane. Think of each representation as being extended indefinitely and we have the idea of a plane as a set of points.

Simple closed curve. A path which begins and ends at the same point and does not cross itself is a simple closed curve. Such a figure has an inside and an outside. A circle is a closed curve. A square is also a closed curve since it is a path that begins and ends at the same point without crossing itself.

Polygon. A polygon is a simple closed curve which is composed of line segments. The square, rectangle, triangle, and parallelogram are polygons.

Circle. The circle is a set of points that belong to the same plane. It is a simple closed curve all points of which are the same distance from the center.

Ray. A ray is a part of a line having an endpoint and extending in one direction indefinitely. A beam of light from a flashlight is a representation of a ray. A picture of a ray begins at an endpoint with an arrow to show direction of indefinite extension.

Angle. An angle is the union of two rays not on the same line but having a common endpoint. The common endpoint is the *vertex* of the angle.

Triangle. A triangle is a polygon formed by the union of three line segments. If all three sides of the triangle are of equal length (congruent), the triangle is an equilateral triangle. If two of the sides are of equal length, it is an isosceles triangle. If all three sides of a triangle are of different length, it is a scalene triangle.

 The meeting of each two sides of this page forms a corner and each corner is a model of a right angle. A right triangle has one right angle associated with it. An isosceles triangle or a scalene triangle can be a right triangle, but an equilateral triangle can have no right angles.

Quadrilaterals. Quadrilaterals are polygons formed by the union of four line segments. A rectangle has four right angles associated with it and its opposite sides are of equal length (congruent). A square is a rectangle with all four sides equal in length. A quadrilateral with opposite sides parallel and of equal lengths, but not necessarily having right angles, is a parallelogram. A rectangle is, therefore, a special kind of parallelogram.

Space figures. A space figure is composed just of the plane regions, forming a simple closed surface. It is thought of as "hollow" with an inside and an outside. Its interior region has volume. This term may be applied generally to three-dimensional figures. The rectangular prism, triangular prism, sphere, cylinder, cone, and pyramid are referred to as space figures. Of these space figures, representations of the rectangular prism and the sphere are commonly within the experience of elementary school children. The rectangular prism may be represented by a box with a cover on it, such as a shoebox. A rectangular prism in which all faces are square is a cube. A globe of the earth and a tennis ball are representations of a sphere.

CHAPTER III

Instructional Procedures

Knowledge of effective techniques of teaching and the ability to put them into practice is judged essential to effective instruction. The effective teacher of arithmetic seeks to use instructional procedures which aid the learner in gaining an understanding of basic ideas, laws, or principles of elementary mathematics; in developing proficiency in various skills and applications in accordance with ability; in developing intellectual curiosity, a discovery attitude, orderly thought, and creativity and flexibility in thinking; in gaining ability to analyze, to make judgments, and to generalize; and in developing a taste and an inclination for the subject and an appreciation of its role in our society.

Principles of Learning

The teacher of arithmetic needs to understand basic principles of learning and to know how to apply them in selecting, organizing, and conducting learning experiences in arithmetic; in selecting and using teaching materials effectively; in using effective means of meeting individual differences; and in evaluating pupil learning. Twentieth-century psychologists have developed several theories of learning. Arithmetic has been a fertile field for the application of some of these.[1] Educators generally agree on some principles of learning that have been derived from these theories.[2] The following are some generally accepted principles of learning which apply to the teaching of arithmetic.

1. Readiness and motivation are important factors in effective

---

[1] Guy T. Buswell, "The Psychology of Learning in Relation to the Teaching of Arithmetic," *The Teaching of Arithmetic*, Fiftieth Yearbook, Part II, National Society for the Study of Education (Chicago: University of Chicago Press, 1951).

[2] Francis G. Lankford, Jr., "Implications of the Psychology of Learning for the Teaching of Mathematics," *The Growth of Mathematical Ideas: Grades K–12*, The Twenty-fourth Yearbook (Washington, D.C.: The National Council of Teachers of Mathematics, 1959).

learning. Readiness is a function not only of mental maturity but also of experience, interest, and attitude. The pupil is best able to learn when he desires to learn and has gained those background skills and understandings which are related to the new concept to be learned.

There is no simple solution to the problem of motivating pupils to learn. The teacher's own enthusiasm for the subject has motivational value. Teachers who understand arithmetic well and present it meaningfully can do a great deal toward motivating pupils to learn arithmetic.

Interesting applications by which the pupil sees purpose in learning activities has motivational value. It is also desirable that students of mathematics should be enthusiastic about its learning because they find the content interesting and thought-provoking. When pupils get insight into the systematic character of the number system, satisfaction in learning results.

2. Learning is understanding rather than mechanical memorization and involves seeing relationships and making appropriate generalizations. Learning arithmetic meaningfully involves understanding the structure, or system of relationships, on which it is based.

Meaningful teaching helps to reveal the relationships and understandings inherent in arithmetic to the learner by means of his own exploration and "discovery." The effective teacher guides the learner into making meaningful generalizations.

One study[3] compared the effectiveness of the drill method with the meaning and generalization method. The pupils in the drill-approach group were taught each of the one hundred addition facts separately with no emphasis on relationships. The pupils in the generalization-approach group were guided in the discovery of generalizations and in their use in learning the facts. The results clearly favored the generalization method.

A more recent study[4] which compared the effectiveness of the "rule" method with the "meaning" method reports similar results in

---

[3] C. Louis Thiele, *Contribution of Generalization to the Learning of Addition Facts,* Contributions to Education, No. 673 (New York: Teacher's College, Columbia University, 1938).

[4] G. H. Miller, "How Effective is the Meaning Method?" *The Arithmetic Teacher,* 4 (March, 1957), 45–49.

favor of the "meaning" method. It is based on data collected from 180 pairs of pupils matched on the basis of intelligence test scores. Both a standardized test and a specially designed "meaning" test were administered. It was concluded that the "meaning" method was more effective in terms of both computational skill and understanding for pupils in the average and above-average intelligence groups.

3. Active participation and "discovery" through varied learning activities and with varied learning materials makes for more effective learning. Elementary school children do not learn best just by being told or being shown how to do something. Pupils learn best when given the opportunity to explore, question, think through, and use varied ways of doing things.

If pupils are to develop an attitude of discovery, an interest in exploration, and independence and creativity of thinking in arithemtic, they must be given numerous opportunities and challenges to learn through these means. Pupils who are actively engaged in exploring various ways of handling a quantitative situation are more likely to be active thinkers in the learning process.

4. Learning is a developmental process by which the learner gradually reaches more mature levels of insight. Learning generally proceeds from the simple to the complex and is a continuous process of integrating previously learned concepts with new concepts.

Each stage in the development of understanding in arithmetic is an outgrowth of a previous stage. Simple ideas are used as a foundation for more refined and generalized ideas. Ideas continue to expand into more mature and abstract concepts.

5. Individuals differ in their rate of learning. Individual differences in interest, attitude, experience, and ability to learn must be taken into consideration if the most effective learning is to be possible for all. Such consideration may result in differentiation in content, teaching pace, learning activities, instructional materials, and reviewing procedures.

6. Practice is necessary for proficiency and is more effective if preceded by understanding of the basic principles of what is being learned. The development of understanding does not eliminate the need for practice. Practice is essential to the automatic mastery of facts and processes of arithmetic. However, the amount of practice and review needed is decreased when arithmetic is mathematically

meaningful to the learner. Practice should be provided in accordance with the needs of the learners.

7. Retention, transfer, and application of learning are increased by emphasis on meaningful generalizations and on the application of generalizations in a variety of situations. Transfer of learning to new situations will be better if the learner has "discovered" relationships and principles and if during learning he has applied these principles in a variety of situations.

8. Knowledge of one's progress contributes to effective learning. Evaluation of progress in learning is important both to the teacher and to the learner. The learner is motivated by indications of progress in learning and is stimulated to compete with himself for further and continued growth in learning. Knowledge of his mistakes provides the learner with evidence as to topics on which restudy is needed. The learner will assume more responsibility for his own progress when kept alert to this progress.

Fostering Discovery, Understanding, and Generalization

Learning arithmetic through "discovery" is judged to contribute to the development of pupils' ability to think mathematically. In the "discovery" approach to learning, the learner is encouraged to use related ideas or principles he already understands in order to make new discoveries. Generally, learning of arithmetic should proceed from specific and varied exploratory experiences to generalization.[5]

Consider the discovery approach to teaching arithmetic as described in a third-grade classroom. The pupils have finished planning eighteen questions on weather. They plan to form committees and each committee is to find the answers to three of the questions. It is now time for arithmetic. The teacher says, "In our study of weather we have eighteen questions and each committee is to study three questions. What do we need to find out?" The children state that they want to find out how many committees are needed. The problem situation is realized and understood by most of the mem-

---

[5] William A. Brownell and Gordon Hendrickson, "How Children Learn Information, Concepts, and Generalizations," *Learning and Instruction,* Forty-ninth Yearbook, Part I, National Society for the Study of Education (Chicago: University of Chicago Press, 1949).

bers of his third-grade class. The teacher writes the problem situation on the chalkboard:

> We have 18 science questions. Each committee will study 3 questions. How many committees are to be made?

The teacher then says, "Each of you may try to find the answer to our problem. Take 18 small cardboard strips from your arithmetic box. You may think of each cardboard strip as standing for a science question. I will come around to see how you use the cardboard strips to help you think about solving our problem. When you finish you may use your number line strip to check your answer. Then try to write a number way to solve the problem."

As pupils work individually, the teacher moves around among them to observe the ways of thinking that are being used. In time she suggests, "Let's talk over ways we used to solve this problem. Who would like to place a picture on the chalkboard to show us how he used the cardboard strips to solve the problem?" A pupil draws this picture on the chalkboard to show how he used the cardboard strips:

The pupil then explains that he has placed 18 strips of paper in a row, made groups of three, and counted the number of groups.

The teacher next asks another child to explain how he thought using the number line. He explains that he began at 18 on the number line and counted backwards by 3's from 18—15, 12, 9, 6, 3, 0. As he counted, he made a tally mark for each group and found 6 groups of three in 18. As the child explains, the teacher marks off groups of three on the chalkboard under the number line which is above the chalkboard.

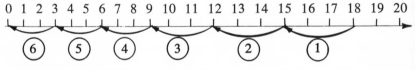

Next the teacher asks, "Would anyone like to show us a number way of thinking?" Several pupils do so, and when they have finished, the class discusses the different number methods. One child writes and explains, "Begin with 18 and subtract 3. Then subtract 3 again and do this until you reach 0. Count the number of 3's subtracted. This is like thinking on the number line. Another child has written:

$$n \times 3 = 18$$
$$n = 6$$

$$
\begin{array}{r}
18 \\
-\ 3 \\ \hline
15 \\
-\ 3 \\ \hline
12 \\
-\ 3 \\ \hline
9 \\
-\ 3 \\ \hline
6 \\
-\ 3 \\ \hline
3 \\
-\ 3 \\ \hline
0
\end{array}
\begin{array}{l}
(1) \\[10pt]
(2) \\[10pt]
(3) \\[10pt]
(4) \\[10pt]
(5) \\[10pt]
(6)
\end{array}
$$

This child explains, "We want to know how many groups of 3 are in 18, so I think n (what number) times 3 equals 18. This is 6."

The class is then guided by the teacher to conclude that finding "how many 3's equal 18" is a process of grouping 18 into six groups with three in each group, which is a process of division. This class of third-grade children has also begun to understand the division operation in this kind of a situation as being related to serial subtraction of a given size group and as the opposite or inverse of multiplication.

Each step in the discovery approach to teaching makes a significant contribution to the child's understanding of arithmetic and to the development of the ability to think mathematically.[6] The discovery approach to teaching arithmetic

1. Begins with a verbal problem situation which may be real or imaginary;
2. Allows the children time to think using concrete and semiconcrete materials and varied number methods;
3. Encourages pupils to show and explain ways of thinking;
4. Provides teacher guidance in helping pupils to note relationships and to generalize;
5. Helps learners to develop independence, a spirit of discovery, and self-confidence.

The place of the teacher in fostering discovery is to lead, guide, and stimulate, but not to show or tell before learners have been challenged and given opportunity to think and explore. Learning by discovery is closely related to the inductive method of learning. Though mathematics is considered to be essentially a deductive science, the development of mathematical principles has been mainly

---

[6] Herbert F. Spitzer, *The Teaching of Arithmetic* (Boston: Houghton Mifflin Company, 1961).

an inductive procedure. After elementary school pupils have had opportunity to discover and arrive at some arithmetical relationships and generalizations, they should also be given experience in thinking about "if . . . then" relationships because it is also important that they gradually learn to do deductive thinking.

Providing Practice in Arithmetic

Teaching arithmetic with major emphasis on meanings does not exclude the use of practice. It does change the position of practice in the total instructional and learning pattern and is judged to reduce the amount of practice needed.[7] Just as a well-conducted arithmetic program provides opportunity to explore and to understand, it also provides sufficient, appropriate, well-spaced practice to achieve mastery of arithmetical principles and procedures necessary to continue successful learning and efficient application of arithmetic.

Nature and place of practice. Practice should be designed to help emphasize the systematic character of number relations and of the number system as well as to help learners achieve automatic mastery of efficient arithmetical procedures. Practice in arithmetic may be viewed as being of two kinds:[8] varied exercises designed to emphasize meaning and application; and repetitive practice exercises designed to fix efficient arithmetical procedures on a mature level.

Varied practice activities which help center attention on meanings basic to arithmetical procedures being learned are an essential part of a well-rounded arithmetic program. After a meaningful approach to a concept has been undertaken, the learner usually will need experience in applying these meanings in order to establish them deeply in his thinking. Varied activities which help to emphasize meanings may include: (a) making drawings to solve exercises; (b) using several number ways of arriving at an answer; (c) noting relationships to complete tables; (d) practicing on a selected aspect of a procedure as deciding when regrouping (borrowing) is needed in a set of subtraction examples; (e) finding the unknown in a

---

[7] William A. Brownell and Charlotte B. Chazal, "The Effects of Premature Drill in Third Grade Arithmetic," *Journal of Educational Research,* 29 (September, 1935), 17–28.

[8] William H. Burton, *The Guidance of Learning Activities* (New York: Appleton-Century-Crofts, Inc., 1952).

mathematical sentence as in $n + 15 = 82$; (f) completing "if . . . then" statements; for example, if $\frac{5}{6} + \frac{5}{6} + \frac{5}{6} = 2\frac{1}{2}$, then ? $\times \frac{5}{6} = 2\frac{1}{2}$; (g) expanding a procedure through the application of an arithmetic law as $9 \times 34 = (9 \times 30) + (9 \times 4) = (270 + 36) = 306$; (h) applying varied ways of checking that emphasize the use of basic laws of arithmetic; for example, $15 \times 27 = 405$ may be checked by thinking $5 \times 27 = 135$; $3 \times 135 = 405$; and (i) taking part in mental exercises which encourage varied ways of thinking to arrive at answers.

Repetitive practice involves the systematic repetition of an arithmetic procedure to develop proficiency and reasonable speed essential to efficient application. It is recommended that repetitive practice not be undertaken until sufficient attention and emphasis has been given to the arithmetical meanings underlying the procedure. The learner is then perfecting procedures through repetitive practice that are intelligible rather than mechanical. It remains important to include competence in computation among the outcomes to be achieved in arithmetic; however, understanding is judged to lessen somewhat the amount of repetitive practice necessary. When a high level of thinking has been reached, then sufficient practice should follow so that the learner perfects mature ways of arriving at answers, develops confidence, and gains a high level of proficiency with arithmetical procedures. Practice both in performing a procedure in an efficient manner and applying it in the solving of problems is needed.

Guiding principles for providing practice. Since the provision of adequate and appropriate practice is such an important part of the total arithmetic program, it is essential that wise judgment be exercised in its provision so that the most efficient results possible may be obtained from this part of the total program.[9] The following principles are generally accepted as guides for the teacher in providing arithmetic practice:

1. Practice should follow rather than precede systematic efforts to develop understanding of an arithmetical procedure. Practice on understood procedures is more efficient in that mastery is more easily obtained and knowledge is more readily retained.

2. Pupils should be helped to realize the importance and value of

[9] John L. Marks, Richard C. Purdy, and Lucien B. Kinney, *Teaching Arithmetic for Understanding* (New York: McGraw-Hill Book Company, Inc., 1958).

practice. The learner can be helped to recognize that proficiency with arithmetic skills facilitates more effective application of arithmetic.

3. Practice should be carefully supervised. It is important that pupils perfect the correct and gradually more mature ways of arriving at answers.

4. Short, well-spaced practice periods are judged to be more efficient than long but infrequent periods of practice.

5. It should be recognized that different pupils may have different practice needs. Practice activities should be individualized in terms of frequency, kind, and amount.

6. The use of arithmetic games to provide practice has value from a motivational standpoint. However, the use of arithmetic games cannot meet the practice needs of all individuals.

7. Practice is likely to be more effective when the learner is kept aware of his progress.

8. Practice should be kept on a thinking level. Varied exercises which center attention on meanings should be interspersed with repetitive practice.

Providing Mental Arithmetic Experiences

Paper and pencil seldom should be necessary for solving or interpreting many simple quantitative situations occurring in activities of everyday life. It is doubtful that even the very best teaching of arithmetic with emphasis only on written computation equips pupils to handle the mental arithmetic situations of life. As used here, mental arithmetic refers to the interpretation or solving of quantitative situations without the aid of paper and pencil. Pupils must be provided with arithmetic experiences which help them to become competent in handling mental arithmetic situations. The effectiveness of systematic provision for developing mental arithmetic ability has been demonstrated.[10]

Mental arithmetic received very little attention in our schools during the first half of the twentieth century. The swing toward little or no emphasis on mental arithmetic about the beginning of the twentieth century seems to have arisen because of an overemphasis on mental arithmetic during the latter part of the nineteenth century. Within the last decade, more attention has been gradually given to the developing mental arithmetic ability; however, more systematic attention to this phase of the total arithmetic program is

---

[10] Frances Flournoy, "The Effectiveness of Instruction in Mental Arithmetic," *Elementary School Journal,* 55 (November, 1954), 148–53.

needed. It is a matter of common experience and observation that life presents many uses for mental arithmetic. A study of the non-occupational uses of arithmetic showed that 70 to 75 per cent of the situations involved mental arithmetic.[11]

Suggestions for developing mental arithmetic ability. In accordance with the probable needs for mental arithmetic in everyday life, the school should provide systematic experiences with mental arithmetic beginning in the primary grades. The following types of exercises, offered systematically, should contribute to the development of the pupils' ability to handle the mental arithmetic situations met in everyday life activities:

1. *Mental computation for exact answers.* This includes learning short-cuts to computation and facility with varied ways of performing addition, subtraction, multiplication, and division. Examples are:

(a) $26 + 58 = (26 + 50) + 8 = 76 + 8 = 84$
(b) $34 + 18 = (34 + 20) - 2 = 54 - 2 = 52$
(c) $75 - 32 = (75 - 30) - 2 = 45 - 2 = 43$
(d) $62 - 28 = (62 - 30) + 2 = 32 + 2 = 34$
(e) $6 \times 17 = (3 \times 17) \times 2 = 2 \times 51 = 102$
(f) $25 \times 12 = (100 \times 12) \div 4 = 300$
(g) $60 \div 4 = (40 \div 4) + (20 \div 4) = 10 + 5 = 15$
(h) $200 \div 8 = 50 \div 2 = 25$

2. *Rounding numbers for use in arriving at approximate answers.* Consideration should be given to (a) learning reasons for and advantages in using rounded numbers, (b) judging when to use rounded numbers and when to use exact numbers, (c) practice in rounding numbers, and (d) practice in estimating answers with rounded numbers.

3. *Mental problem-solving experiences.* This practice may be with problems read silently by the pupil and solved without the aid of paper and pencil. These problem-solving experiences should frequently involve just listening and solving problems read aloud by the teacher but not seen in written form by the pupils. Also of value is pupil experience in constructing verbal problems from everyday experiences to be read aloud by pupils for others to solve without the aid of paper and pencil.

---

[11] Edwin Wandt and Gerald W. Brown, "Non-Occupational Uses of Mathematics," *The Arithmetic Teacher,* 4 (October, 1957), 151–54.

4. *Interpreting quantitative statements.* This should include the realization of the importance of properly interpreting quantitative statements found in reading reference materials (such as "The height of the mountain is 8,276 feet," or "The size of the farm is 10 acres"). Pupils need experience in selecting suitable "reference measures" (areas, heights, distances, quantities from their own experiences) and in using reference measures to clarify quantitative statements.[12] A set of reference measures peculiar to a certain locality should be worked out by each class under the guidance of the teacher and a chart made for easy reference. The chart might include such information as "500 people: students in our school, 40 feet: length of our classroom, 200 miles: distance from our city to the capital city of our state."

Developing Ability to Solve
Verbal Problems

Development of the ability to interpret and solve quantitative situations met in daily life now and in the future is an important objective of arithmetic instruction. *Problem* as used here refers to a socially significant quantitative situation in which certain data are given, or are recognized, and about which a question is asked or perceived. The problem solver must realize the relationships in the quantitative situation, determine an arithmetical way of expressing each relationship, and perform the operation which enables him to find the answer.

Problems may be from actual experiences in which a question is realized and essential related data are collected and organized into a problem situation. However, many social problems included in the arithmetic program are situations described in the basic arithmetic text being used. These problems are generally related to the experiences of most children and so are within their understanding. However, in order to stimulate interest, occasional use might be made of problem situations that are unusual, imaginative, and different from problems of everyday experiences. The use of verbal problems in a textbook provides a variety of arithmetic applications that would not be available if only firsthand experiences were de-

---

[12] Herbert F. Spitzer, *op. cit.,* pp. 235–37.

pended upon to furnish problem-solving situations in the arithmetic program.

Factors influencing pupil ability to solve verbal problems. The teacher is in a better position to develop pupils' problem-solving ability when she is thoroughly aware of the various factors which relate to pupil success in solving quantitative problems. Inability in one or a combination of several of these factors may cause a pupil difficulty in learning to solve verbal problems.

Understanding the four number operations—addition, subtraction, multiplication, and division—is essential in order that the learner may see the relationship between the described problem situation and the operation needed in solving it. The pupil must have an adequate general reading vocabulary. He must be able to read with comprehension, visualize the situation, note details, separate relevant from irrelevant data, remember the question asked while rereading related data, and note the relationships in the problem situation. Ability to express problem relationships as arithmetical sentences is essential in problem-solving. The learner must, of course, have adequate knowledge of such essential information as number facts, relationships of commonly used measures, arithmetical symbols, formulas, the technical vocabulary of arithmetic, and the use of graphs and tables. In addition, an interest in arithmetic and in learning to solve verbal problems plays a significant role in problem-solving ability. Mastery of computational procedures, an orderly arrangement of written work, and carefully performed computation must be encouraged.

Of the various factors related to problem-solving ability, studies of the relationship between problem-solving and intelligence, as well as between problem-solving and arithmetical understanding, indicate that these two factors are most significant in relation to problem-solving ability. Reading ability has also been found to be rather closely related to achievement in problem-solving.[13]

Suggestions for improving problem-solving ability. The following suggestions are commonly recommended for improving problem-solving ability:

1. *Using verbal problems for introducing new arithmetic concepts.* The problem provides a setting for exploring the new arith-

---

[13] Leland H. Erickson, "Certain Ability Factors and Their Effect on Arithmetic Achievement," *The Arithmetic Teacher,* 5 (December, 1958), 287–93.

metic topic or skill through using a variety of materials and number methods for solving the problem situation. As a result the learner gains mathematical understanding, perceives relationships, learns to relate the arithmetic concept to a problem situation in which it is used, realizes the significance of the mathematical concept when it is known to be the most efficient way of solving the problem, and gains confidence in his own ability to solve problems.

2. *Constructing original problems.* Experience in constructing original problems helps to make the learner more sensitive to the needs for arithmetic in everyday life. Experience in constructing appropriate questions about known facts should contribute greatly to the learner's ability to read a verbal problem and note the relationship of what is asked to what is given. The construction of original problems should follow the introduction of a new concept through a problem situation. After pupils have solved given problems in a variety of ways and have studied the relationships involved, participation in the construction of original problems further aids them in relating a problem situation to the operation needed for solving it. At first, problems should be constructed cooperatively, with the teacher guiding the activity. Pupils gradually will learn to construct problems independently. Sometimes pupils should be given data to be used in constructing a problem about a particular situation. On other occasions pupils may be given a particular situation as buying lunch, selling carnival tickets, or sharing cookies and be asked to gather their own data and to construct a problem involving an indicated operation.

3. *Learning to state mathematical sentences or equations to express problem relationships.* When the problem solver has recognized the relationships in a problem situation, he must then be able to express the relationship arithmetically before proceeding to solve the problem.

As pupils learn the meaning of addition, subtraction, multiplication, and division, they learn to express these concepts in arithmetic sentences or equations, as $7 + 5 = 12$; $9 - 3 = 6$; $4 \times 2 = 8$; $12 \div 3 = 4$. The equation is a means of expressing the situation in a verbal problem in the language of arithmetic. The writing of an equation about a problem situation requires careful reading and understanding of the problem. The following are examples of such equations:

Jane is helping the teacher put 48 books on 4 shelves with an equal number of books on each shelf. How many books will Jane put on each shelf?

Equation: $n = 48 \div 4$

Solution: $n = 12$

Joe wants to buy a toy airplane that costs 23 cents. He has 14 cents. How much more money does he need?

Equation: $14 + n = 23$

Solution: $\quad n = 23 - 14$

$\quad\quad n = 9$

Note: To solve the equation the pupil needs to understand that when the sum and one addend are given, the other addend is found by subtraction.

4. *Solving verbal problems read orally.* In this procedure the teacher usually reads the problem aloud just once while pupils listen. Pupils solve each problem and record the answer. It is suggested that the problem be read only once to encourage attentiveness; also, a second reading would disturb the thinking of those pupils who begin solving the problem after the first reading. Such problems are usually kept brief and should involve small numbers so that learners can concentrate on the problem situation and the computation required is not so great a factor in problem-solving success. Pupils also may receive many of the benefits of this oral activity by listening to the reading of the problems and then performing the computation, using paper and pencil if needed. There may be considerable transfer from careful listening to a problem read well orally to attentive, independent reading of problems.[14]

Short practice periods of ten to twenty minutes once or twice a week for solving problems in this fashion should contribute much to building power in problem-solving. It is believed that even children in the first grade can be given more problem-solving experiences if the teacher will frequently read or describe problems orally and encourage pupils to think through the answer.

5. *Solving problems in a variety of ways.* Pupils at all grade levels should be given some experience in solving problems in various ways, as by dramatizing, using objects, drawing pictures, and using

---

[14] Frances Flournoy, "The Effectiveness of Instruction in Mental Arithmetic," *Elementary School Journal,* 55 (November, 1954), 148–53.

a variety of number methods. Through varied approaches to problem-solving, pupils have experiences which enable them to visualize problem situations more clearly, realize problem relationships, and determine efficient number procedures for solving. Varied approaches to problem-solving may also contribute to greater interest in problem-solving and more confidence in one's ability to solve verbal problems.

6. *Special exercises with problems.* Various special exercises which center attention on aspects of reading and noting problem relationships have been recommended as techniques for improving problem-solving ability. Procedures suggested include:

(a) Formal problem analysis: after the whole problem has been read, the pupil may be encouraged to state the question, the given facts that are needed in answering the question, and the procedures for solving the problem. This method should be used only occasionally. Its value lies in encouraging the pupil to read carefully and in familiarizing the child with how a problem is constructed. Frequent use of the procedure has not proved to be of value for it consumes much time and may be discouraging to some pupils.[15]

(b) Stating the operation needed in solving: this relieves the child of the computational aspect of problem solving and centers attention on the importance of recognizing the correct operation for solving.

(c) Studying problems without numbers: some pupils seize upon numbers used in problems and begin performing various operations before reading the problem carefully. In this procedure attention is centered on the described situation and only the related operation is to be selected.

(d) Supplying a missing question: to help pupils understand the relationship between question asked and facts that are given, pupils may be asked to supply an appropriate question for problems without questions.

(e) Supplying a missing fact: this technique also centers the pupil's attention on the nature of a problem. This procedure encourages careful reading and problem understanding and visualization.

(f) Deciding what given fact is not needed for solving a problem: this technique encourages the pupil to look carefully for the relationship between what is asked and what facts are needed in solving a problem.

(g) Estimating answers to problems and then solving for the exact answer: when this procedure is used, the learner thinks through a problem twice. First, he uses rounded numbers and is encouraged to think

---

[15] Paul R. Hanna, *Arithmetic Problem-Solving: A Study of the Relative Effectiveness of Three Methods of Problem Solving,* Contributions to Education (New York: Teacher's College, Columbia University, 1929).

about the reasonableness of his answer. Then he reads the problem again and solves for an exact answer which he compares with his rounded answers. Systematic attention should be given to teaching pupils how to round numbers and estimate answers as it is a skill needed in everyday life.

(h) Stating the hidden question: when learning to solve two-step problems, many pupils have difficulty because they do not recognize an unstated question which must be answered before the answer to the stated question can be found. In the use of this procedure, attention is centered mainly on stating the hidden question in a two-step problem.

7. *Noting computational deficiencies and taking steps to improve.* If a pupil can generally select a correct procedure for solving and yet makes errors in his computation, remedial steps should be taken for helping him to improve his computational skill.

8. *Problem projects.* Individual, small-group, or whole-class problem projects may help to make problem-solving more interesting. In this procedure pupils are first led to recognize a problem and then are given guidance in gathering and organizing data needed in solving it. Examples of such problem projects are:

(a) Finding out how much it costs to keep a dog;
(b) Laying off a baseball diamond;
(c) Increasing punch and cookie recipes for a party;
(d) Buying refreshments for a class party;
(e) Planting a garden;
(f) Keeping a record in a Red Cross fund-raising campaign;
(g) Making a scale model of planet distances from the sun;
(h) Making an historical number line;
(i) Figuring baseball averages of boys in the class.

9. *Practice in problem-solving.* After understanding is established, pupils need considerable practice in problem-solving in order to reach a high level of proficiency.

10. *Progress tests.* Systematic giving of problem tests of eight, ten, or more problems is recommended. Pupils may keep a bar graph of problem-solving test results over a period of time to note their progress.

Place of the Arithmetic Textbook

The well-written arithmetic textbook introduces topics with exploratory opportunities relating to significant problem situations and leads pupils to discovery and generalization. Meaningful illustrations and probing questions help to guide learners in their thinking about arithmetical relationships and principles. The textbook aids the teacher in providing appropriate practice, application, and evaluation. An arithmetic textbook with its accompanying teacher's manual is the best guide the individual teacher has regarding arithmetic understanding and skills to be taught and the appropriate sequence for presentation.

In order that learners may be challenged and given opportunity to explore and discover on their own, a carefully planned and guided pre-book learning experience should be provided when introducing a new arithmetic topic or a new phase of a topic. The pre-book activity should usually pose a problem situation, provide pupils with an opportunity to explore the situation by using a variety of visual materials and number ways of thinking, and include teacher-guided pupil consideration of various ways of dealing with the quantitative situation. After a pre-book activity in which they have been challenged to think and have used concrete and semiconcrete materials as aids to understanding mathematical ideas, pupils are ready to read with understanding and to carry out the textbook learning exercises.

The use of a single textbook, however, cannot adequately meet the needs of all learners. It is important that the teacher supplement the textbook with varied visual materials and other printed materials, and take advantage of daily opportunities to use arithmetic and make its learning significant. In order to make provisions for individual differences, the teacher may need to make appropriate adjustments in content taught, teaching methods used, practice provided, and teaching pace.

Using Visual Learning Materials

With much emphasis on meaningful arithmetic teaching, the use of visual arithmetic materials has received considerable attention in recent years. As used here, *visual materials* refer to real, manipulative, pictorial, and projected materials. Specific ideas for and sources of such learning materials are described in Chapter IV. The teacher needs to exercise careful judgment in the selection and use of visual arithmetic materials. Purposes and general principles for using such materials should be well understood.

Purposes in using visual arithmetic materials. Visual materials should aid the teacher in accomplishing instructional goals. Visual arithmetic materials may be used (a) for exploratory and discovery purposes when new concepts are being introduced; (b) for pupil demonstration of understanding; (c) for guided study of arithmetical relationships; (d) as reference material for pupils; (e) in reviewing meanings; and (f) for checking or verification.

Guiding principles for using visual arithmetic materials. It is extremely important that the teacher know when and how to use such visual aids.

1. The use of visual materials should be kept on a thinking level, so that pupils are not just manipulating objects without gaining insight into the basic arithmetical principles involved. The teacher should give guidance as to the correct, efficient way to use various visual materials and should direct pupil thinking regarding the basic principles being illustrated.

2. Visual materials should serve to carry pupils from the concrete level to an abstract level of thinking; and it should be kept clearly in mind that the end product desired is the ability to think and operate abstractly.

3. Appropriate visual materials have value in teaching arithmetic concepts at all levels in the elementary school and may be used to help fast learners, as well as the average and slow learners, to develop an understanding of arithmetic.

4. Although all pupils will profit from the use of visual materials, pupils vary greatly as to how long and how frequently they will need to use such materials in the study of a particular arithmetical idea. This variation in need for visual materials should be considered carefully when planning instruction.

5. Organizational or summary charts should generally not be used until after pupils have had a more direct experience with ideas included in them.

6. Whenever possible, materials for individual pupil use should be made available. When both an individual size and a class demonstration size of a particular material are available, it is generally best to allow pupils to use small-size materials first, and then to follow the idea as illustrated and explained by a pupil or by the teacher using the large-size material.

7. In general, there should be an intermediate stage between the concrete or semiconcrete and the abstract stage of learning about a

particular concept. During this intermediate stage, pupils may be encouraged to use both the visual material and a way of thinking with numbers. Pupils should be encouraged to think and to operate abstractly as soon as they see the relationship between the visual material procedure and the abstract procedure.

A number of studies have been reported regarding the effectiveness of using specific visual arithmetic materials. In general, the groups using the visual materials have evidenced a greater gain in arithmetic achievement. However, carefully designed experiments to evaluate the effect of visual arithmetic materials on arithmetic understanding have not been reported. Contribution of visual arithmetic materials to understanding has of course been informally noted by many teachers.

Diagnosis and Remedial Teaching

When it is evident that a pupil is not making satisfactory progress in learning arithmetic, the teacher should take carefully planned steps to identify specific learning difficulties, diagnose causes, determine what reteaching is needed, and provide varied remedial experiences. If learning difficulties are allowed to continue without remedial steps being taken, a very serious learning problem results.

Causes of pupils' learning difficulties relate to general level of mental ability, emotional maturity, physical factors, reading ability, degree of arithmetical understanding, attentiveness, and work habits. Various means of analyzing difficulties and diagnosing causes have been reported.[16] Recommended means include:

1. Carefully observe the pupil at work to note interest, concentration, work habits, emotional factors, and physical factors related to achievement.

2. Analyze his written work to note knowledge of facts and procedures, type of errors.

3. Carefully consider oral responses to note pupil's level of thinking and understanding.

4. Interview the pupil to explore his interest in learning and to check his understanding of basic arithmetical principles.

5. Use diagnostic tests covering a particular topic with rows or sets of examples arranged in order of difficulty from the simplest phase of

---

[16] Leo J. Brueckner, "Diagnosis in Arithmetic," *Educational Diagnosis*, Thirty-fourth Yearbook, National Society for the Study of Education (Bloomington, Ill.: Public School Publishing Company, 1935).

the particular topic to the most difficult phase which has already been introduced.

While the latter procedure does help to identify the level at which a pupil can succeed on a particular topic and types of errors, it does not reveal *why* the pupil is having learning difficulties. The use of the more clinical techniques are necessary to determine causes of learning difficulties. General procedures recommended for use in remedial teaching are:

1. Secure the interest of the learner and help him to see purpose in learning arithmetic.
2. Begin reteaching at a point where the pupil will succeed, then gradually proceed to more difficult levels.
3. Put the emphasis on understanding, not mechanical procedures.
4. Make extensive use of visual aids to learning.
5. Use a variety of ways of learning: games, drawings, charts, dramatization, oral work, and teacher-directed reading of printed materials.
6. Individualize practice.
7. Keep periods of remedial work short.
8. Provide opportunity for pupil to engage in some of the regular class activities, with some progress in learning new topics along with others.
9. Give much encouragement and appropriate praise for progress.
10. Help the pupil to keep some record of progress; the use of selected exercises in a workbook may provide a good record of progress.

Providing Extension Experiences in Arithmetic

Increasing attention to enrichment of content and provision of power-building experiences in arithmetic has been evidenced since the early 1950's.[17] Enrichment and power-building experiences provide horizontal extension of the basic core of arithmetic content and activities usually included at each grade level. As used here, such experiences are not intended to include vertical acceleration by teaching the fast learners some of the basic arithmetic understandings and skills generally taught at the next highest grade level. However, a program of vertical acceleration for some pupils may be desirable and is discussed in Chapter V. Arithmetic enrichment and power-building experiences may help to broaden knowledge,

---

[17] Foster E. Grossnickle and Leo J. Brueckner, *Discovering Meanings in Arithmetic* (Philadelphia: The John C. Winston Co., 1959).

stir appreciation, promote creativeness, stimulate intense interest, and develop greater insight into the nature of mathematics. As the basic topics of arithmetic are taught, appropriate extension exercises for enrichment and power-building may be provided.

Horizontal extension in arithmetic includes (a) providing historical information about numeration systems, fractions used long ago, and the development of measures; (b) working with other number bases; (c) studying interesting number patterns or sequences; (d) finding missing digits in algorisms; (e) using varied computational and checking procedures, such as lattice multiplication, equal addition of 10 to subtract when regrouping is needed, and checking by casting out 9's; (f) clock arithmetic; (g) working recreational arithmetic puzzles, riddles, and games; (h) unusual measures; (i) mental shortcuts; (j) research on special topics as the cost of keeping a dog, the averages of baseball players, and the functioning of computing machines; (k) studying foreign currencies; and (l) studying interesting applications of arithmetic, as in meteorology, navigation, banking, and insurance. Sources of these and other arithmetic extension ideas are presented in Chapter IV on materials of instruction.

CHAPTER IV

Materials for Arithmetic Instruction

A variety of appropriate instructional materials, carefully selected and wisely used, should contribute greatly to effective teaching of elementary school mathematics. Varied instructional materials motivate learning, provide for more active participation of the learner, and aid in the development of understanding. The end product desired is the ability to think and perform on an abstract level with understanding of the underlying mathematical principles. Several kinds of instructional materials are valuable in guiding the learner through the exploration, discovery, symbolization and generalization stages of learning. Instructional materials may be classified as: (a) manipulative and pictorial materials; (b) printed instructional materials; (c) projection materials; and (d) community resources.

It is not possible to present here a detailed description of all the available materials of each type. An excellent bulletin on commercial materials for the teaching of mathematics at the elementary, junior high, and senior high levels is *A Guide to the Use and Procurement of Teaching Aids for Mathematics,* by Emil J. Berger and Donovan A. Johnson, published by The National Council of Teachers of Mathematics, Washington, D.C.

Manipulative and Pictorial Materials

Manipulative aids are materials which can be seen, handled, and manipulated. These include objects such as chairs, books, bottle tops, lollipop sticks, clock faces, measuring spoons, rulers, and scales. These also include special devices as the abacus, number line, place value boxes, and fractional cutouts. Manipulative materials are frequently used during the exploratory and discovery stage of learning. Later pupils may again use such materials to demonstrate understanding of a concept or to verify answers.

Pictorial materials include models, pictures, diagrams, charts, graphs, and tables. (Films and filmstrips which are also pictorial materials will be discussed in another section of this chapter.) Pictorial materials may be used to help the learner perceive a relationship between the concrete representation and the symbolic representation of an idea. Pictorial materials are also excellent for pointing out relationships, for serving as reference materials, and for summary purposes.

Manipulative and pictorial materials may be either teacher-made, commercial, or both. Appropriate materials in sufficient quantity should be available in every classroom or easily obtainable from a materials room in the school. An excellent discussion of use and sources of visual arithmetic materials is recommended for reading.[1] The following is a list of suggested materials related to major topics of elementary school mathematics:

1. *Number, numeration, and operation:* (a) counters for counting and grouping, as bottle tops; (b) counting frames; (c) ten groups, as small sticks with rubber band to hold each ten group; (d) number, numeral, number word chart, 1–10; place value chart with places named as thousands; $10 \times 10 \times 10$, and 10^3; (e) numeral cards or chart; (f) hundreds chart; (g) teens chart; (h) simplified abacus; (i) domino cards; (j) place value pocket chart or device; (k) number line strips (whole numbers); (l) hundred peg board; (m) set or family fact-building charts; (n) fact finders; (o) felt or flannel board with symbols and materials for grouping; (p) simplified cardboard slide rule; (q) relationship chart for addition and subtraction; and (r) relationship chart for multiplication and division.

2. *Fractions:* (a) number line strips or charts (common and decimal fractions); (b) fraction cutouts and pupil kits; (c) fraction strip charts or boards; (d) decimal fraction place value pocket chart or device; (e) whole number-decimal fraction chart with places named as hundreds, 10×10, or 10^2 and hundredths, $\frac{1}{10} \times \frac{1}{10}$, or $(\frac{1}{10})^2$; (f) common and decimal fraction relationship chart or board; (g) decimal and per cent chart or board; and (h) tenths strips and hundredths chart or board (hundred squares).

3. *Geometry and measures:* (a) ruler; (b) yardstick; (c) tape measure; (d) chart showing linear measurement relationships (actual size) as inches in foot, feet in yard; (e) sets of play money;

---

[1] Clarence Ethel Hardgrove and Ben A. Sueltz, "Instructional Materials," *Instruction in Arithmetic,* Twenty-fifth Yearbook (Washington, D.C.: National Council of Teachers of Mathematics, 1960).

(f) sets of measuring spoons or cups; (g) thermometer (on poster-board) with movable ribbon; (h) real thermometer; (i) small-weight scales; (j) classroom sets of standard measures for cup, half-pint, pint, quart, gallon; (k) standard peck and bushel measures; (l) money (actual size) relationship chart; (m) clock face with adjustable hands and a schoolroom clock; (n) calendar with movable parts for name of month, year, and day of month; (o) egg cartons and parts of cartons; (p) sets of miscellaneous items as checkbook, deposit slip, sales slip, utility bill, receipts, road map, old speedometer and mileage indicator, play telephone, play cash register, timetables, rain gauge, directional compass; (q) square inch, square foot, square yard chart; (r) perimeter-area board; (s) cubic foot model; (t) set of one-inch cubes; (u) cardboard model of circle, triangle, square, rectangle, parallelogram; (v) peg board for string outlining of plane geometric figures, and (w) model of cube, sphere, cylinder, cone, and rectangular prism.

Teacher-made visual materials. The teacher can prepare or collect a variety of useful materials for the teaching of arithmetic. Descriptions of a few materials for use in the primary and intermediate grades are presented below:

1. *Counting kits.* Each child in the primary grades should have a supply of objects to count and group as sticks, bottle caps, and cardboard disks. Pupils can help the teacher collect these materials.

2. *Ten groups.* Lollipop sticks, tongue depressors or other similar items may be cleaned, dyed bright colors, and grouped in tens with rubber bands.

3. *Abacus.* An abacus can be made by using wooden beads strung ten on each of three vertical wires fastened to an old picture frame. A coat hanger can also be straightened and rearranged so that there are three vertical wires with ten beads on each. Small clothespins can be used to hold up groups of beads on each wire as needed.

4. *Ten 10's or 100 board.* Mark off ten horizontal rows of squares with ten squares in each row on a piece of quarter-inch plywood that is about 30 inches square. Screw a small hook near the top of each square. Write each numeral (1–100) as large as possible on one side of milk bottle tops or round tags which may be purchased; leave other side of each tag blank.

5. *Fact finders.* A coat hanger or heavy wire with the ends turned

back may be used to hold counters (10–18), such as wooden beads or small clothespins.

6. *Ten and ones chart* (*11–19*). In making, begin with 19 at the bottom of the chart. A group of ten dots may be colored or pasted in a horizontal row; then leave a space and put on nine more dots in the same row. Dots in each row should be carefully matched in spacing with dots in each of the other rows. The numerals for each teens number represented in rows can be written in a column to the extreme right of the chart.

7. *Place value chart.* Heavy paper which can be folded to form pockets may be used. Paper may be folded up and taped to form one pocket, if to be used only for place value, or three or four pockets if to be used for simple adding, subtracting, multiplying, and dividing. The pocket for each place (tens, ones) should be 12 to 16 inches across. Tens and ones pockets may be placed on one large chart, and other sections (hundreds, thousands) be placed in the proper position and used as needed. The name of each place should be printed at the top of the pocket chart. Paper strips about ½ inch wide and 3 inches long may be cut to put in pockets as counters.

8. *Numeral cards.* A set of cards for the basic numerals, 1–10, may be made. Each card should be large enough that the numeral can easily be seen from any part of the classroom. The place to begin in writing the numeral should be clearly marked with an arrow or dashes at the beginning of the numeral. The numeral may be placed on the lefthand side of the card and a pattern of dots to stand for the number may be placed to the right of the card.

9. *Fraction kit.* Using construction paper of any color or colors, the teacher can ditto sheets of circles which have been divided into halves, thirds, fourths, eighths (as is needed at a particular grade level). At least one whole circle should also be included. (Pupils can cut out circles and parts.) Each set of fraction cutouts can be placed in an envelope. Each pupil will have an individual fraction kit.

10. *Multiplication and division grid.* Use posterpaper or plywood that is about 30 inches square. Space for index strips should be drawn across the top and down the side as shown. Then ten rows with ten squares in each row should be marked off. If posterpaper is being used, products are printed in as shown. If plywood is used,

	0	1	2	3	4	5	6	7	8	9
0	0	0	0	0	0	0	0	0	0	0
1	0	1	2	3	4	5	6	7	8	9
2	0	2	4	6	8	10	12	14	16	18
3	0	3	6	9	12	15	18	21	24	27
4	0	4	8	12	16	20	24	28	32	36
5	0	5	10	15	20	25	30	35	40	45
6	0	6	12	18	24	30	36	42	48	54
7	0	7	14	21	28	35	42	49	56	63
8	0	8	16	24	32	40	48	56	64	72
9	0	9	18	27	36	45	54	63	72	81

the products may be written on round tags which may be hung on a small hook near the top of each square. A product is located, as in 6 × 8, by locating 6 on the lefthand side and going across on this row to a point which is under the 8 column. In this square is the product of 6 × 8, or 48.

11. *Fraction chart or board.* A large piece of chart paper may be used with slits cut on each side for inserting the ends of four to six strips. One whole strip and a set of fraction strips can be made from construction paper or posterpaper. The fractional parts of a strip should be named as shown in the following illustration.

Fractional strips may be inserted and removed as needed. The frame could be made of lightweight wood with narrow strips mounted across the board for sliding fractional parts in and out. With a board frame, individual fractional parts can be used so that a one-half part and two one-fourth parts can be inserted together if desired.

12. *Fraction discs.* Two cardboard circles the same size (about 12 inches in diameter) may be made for pairs of fractions as ¼ and ⅛. One circle may be white; the other can be any other color. Each

fractional part on a circle should be named as ¼ or ⅛. Slit each circle along one of the line divisions to the center. Insert one circle in another and rotate to show relationships.

13. *Decimal fraction–common fraction chart.* A chart or board can be prepared to show relationships. A set of named fractional strips or parts for a portion of the chart is shown below.

⅕		⅕		⅕		⅕		⅕	
⅒	⅒	⅒	⅒	⅒	⅒	⅒	⅒	⅒	⅒
.1	.1	.1	.1	.1	.1	.1	.1	.1	.1
.10	.10	.10	.10	.10	.10	.10	.10	.10	.10

14. *Decimal fraction chart.* A chart, with places named as shown, may be prepared with units as the pivot point and extending as far to the left and right of the units place as desired.

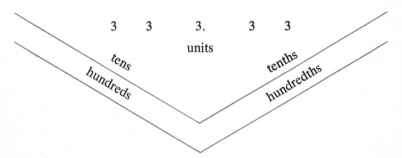

A similar chart can be prepared using 10 × 10 in the hundreds place and ⅒ × ⅒ in the hundredths place. Later 10^2 for hundred and $\frac{1}{10}^2$ for hundredths may be used.

15. *Fraction number line charts.* A large piece of posterpaper

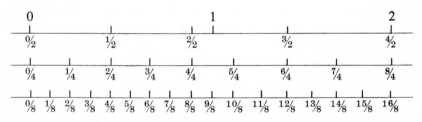

may be used for one fraction family as shown. Another chart could be prepared for halves, thirds, and sixths. A chart for halves, fifths, and tenths would also be useful.

16. *Square yard chart.* The chart should be 3 feet by 3 feet. Nine square feet blocks should be marked off. One of the square foot parts can be marked off to show 12 rows with 12 square inches in each row.

17. *Cubic foot and cubic inch models.* Six cardboard one-foot squares may be cut. Each of these squares can be marked off into 144 equal squares. The six cardboard squares should then be taped together to form a cubic foot model. By looking at the six-sided model the pupil could see that there would be 144 cubes in a layer and 12 layers or 1728 cubic inches in one cubic foot. Cubic inch models can also be made by using six square inch pieces of cardboard and taping these together at the edges to form a cubic inch.

Commercial materials. A wide variety of commercial materials for use in the teaching of arithmetic is available. Catalogs may be secured from companies which offer arithmetic instructional aids. These sources include:

Milton Bradley Company
74 Park Street
Springfield, Mass.

Creative Playthings
5 University Place
New York, N.Y.

Cuisenaire Company of America, Inc.
246 East Forty-Sixth Street
New York, N.Y.

Daintee Toys, Inc.
230 Steuben Street
Brooklyn 5, N.Y.

J. L. Hammett Company
Kendall Square
Cambridge, Mass.

Houghton Mifflin Company
2 Park Street
Boston, Mass.

Ideal School Supply Company
8312 Birkhoff Avenue
Chicago, Ill.

Judy Company
310 North Second Street
Minneapolis, Minn.

W. M. Welch Scientific Company
1515 Sedgwick Street
Chicago, Ill.

Holt, Rinehart & Winston, Inc.
383 Madison Avenue
New York, N.Y.

A pamphlet which gives sources of arithmetic teaching aids and sources of free and inexpensive materials is *Chicago Schools Journal Supplement: Mathematical Teaching Aids,* compiled by Joseph J. Urbancek and published by Chicago Teachers College, Chicago, Ill. The National Council of Teachers of Mathematics publication, *A Guide to the Use and Procurement of Teaching Aids for Mathematics,* presents a well-organized listing of available commercial materials and sources.

Printed Instructional Materials

Printed materials are the most commonly used instructional materials. These include textbooks, teaching manuals, workbooks, supplementary books, and pamphlets.

Textbooks, teacher's manuals, and workbooks. The modern arithmetic textbook, with its accompanying teacher's manual, is an invaluable instructional material. It provides a good coverage of basic topics to be taught with systematic attention to underlying mathematical principles.

The well-prepared arithmetic textbook should provide (1) an exploratory-discovery approach to teaching and learning; (2) grading of topics, or phases of topics, according to difficulty; (3) a spiral organization of content from grade to grade to promote continually expanding insight into basic mathematical concepts; (4) thorough treatment of selected phases of topics at each level or grade; (5) social situations to emphasize the usefulness of arithmetic; (6) careful development of basic mathematical principles and relationships; (7) appropriate illustrations or diagrams, charts, relationship tables, questions, and exercises to guide thinking and lead to significant generalizations; (8) exercises to develop problem-solving ability; (9) appropriate and varied practice exercises to develop computational skill; (10) numerous and varied verbal problems for the application of arithmetic; (11) diagnostic and remedial exercises; (12) extension and enrichment exercises; (13) variations in content for meeting individual needs; (14) systematic review; and (15) systematic testing for evaluating learning.

Teacher's manuals which accompany arithmetic textbooks have been greatly improved in recent years. Many of these manuals now include background information for the teacher, major ideas or understandings to be emphasized in each chapter or unit, suggestions for the teaching of each lesson, additional and varied exercises to aid in meeting individual differences, additional tests, and a grade placement chart for the series. Some manuals include suggestions for games, teacher-made visual materials, sources of commercial materials, sources of films and filmstrips, and a bibliography of recommended supplementary books for the pupils and for the teacher.

Though most arithmetic textbooks provide an adequate program for the development of arithmetic understandings and skills, workbooks are sometimes used to provide additional and varied practice on computation and problem-solving, as well as additional tests for evaluating pupil learning.

The consumable arithmetic workbook or worktext which is commonly prepared for Grades 1 and 2 is an important part of a basic textbook series. It is the basic arithmetic textbook for these grades and has been carefully prepared. With its accompanying teacher's manual, it is a very valuable instructional material. The content, organization, general vocabulary, and arithmetic vocabulary used in the text for Grades 1 and 2 should lead smoothly into the use of the third-grade textbook. Since such a worktext for Grades 1 and 2 provides a foundation for the use of the third-grade textbook, it is recommended that all three texts should be of the same published series as the textbooks used in the other elementary grades.

The various publishers of arithmetic textbook series provide information regarding major features of their publications: content, scope, and sequence of topics by grade levels. This information is readily available in the form of bulletins and charts which publishers usually furnish free of charge.

Programmed materials. A new educational device is the arrangement of selected topics in a series of short fill-in or multiple choice statements which proceed logically from one another. The statements are arranged in order of increasing difficulty. The student reads each statement and supplies the answer. The correct response is also given (on another page) and the student compares each answer with the correct one before proceeding to the next statement. Material so arranged is referred to as a *program*. These materials are generally designed to be used on teaching machines, but some are available in workbook form.

Although such materials do provide a very systematic presentation and permit each learner to progress at his own rate of speed, they represent a rather stilted approach to learning. There may be too little opportunity for exploration and creative thinking. Such materials may also tend to encourage memorization rather than true understanding of abstract concepts and relationships. No careful research results have yet been published which compare the effectiveness of programmed materials with that of a well-planned textbook combined with a consistent effort to provide for individual differences. Nevertheless, if programmed materials are used in proper relation with other instructional materials and procedures, they may prove a most valuable teaching aid.

Supplementary books and pamphlets. The alert teacher will make use of supplementary books and pamphlets which are useful in enriching the arithmetic program and in stimulating interest in the field of mathematics. Through the use of supplementary materials presented by the teacher and explored independently by pupils, various arithmetic topics may be pursued to greater depth, interesting and varied exercises and activities may be carried out, and additional knowledge not included in the basic arithmetic program may be gained. Supplementary arithmetic materials include books and pamphlets of various kinds. There are story books that present number uses and concepts in interesting ways and historical accounts of the development of counting, the numeration system, algorisms, fractions, decimals, and measures. There are informational books about mathematics, and particularly about geometry. Numerous pamphlets or paperback books contain recreational puzzles, riddles, and exercises. A few carefully prepared booklets of exercises on other number bases, unusual measures, ancient algorisms, number patterns, and explorations in geometry are available. Numerous pamphlets on the use of mathematics in banking, navigation, insurance, medicine, and meteorology may be secured. A book which provides the teacher with numerous ideas for stimulating interest in arithmetic through recreational and unusual arithmetic activities is, *Practical Classroom Procedures for Enriching Arithmetic,* by Herbert F. Spitzer, and published by the Webster Publishing Company, St. Louis, Mo. A series of enrichment booklets for use by pupils in Grades 3–8 are published by Harper & Row, Publishers, New York. These booklets were prepared by Harold D. Larsen and are entitled, *Enrichment Program for Arithmetic.* An annotated bibliography of supplementary books on elementary mathematics may be consulted.[2]

A series of workbooks for use in extending mathematical thinking in Grades 4, 5 and 6 are published by Ginn and Company, Boston. They were prepared by John L. Marks, James R. Smart, and Irene Sauble. Webster Publishing Company has published a set

---

[2] Clarence Ethel Hardgrove, *The Elementary and Junior High School Library* (Washington, D.C.: The National Council of Teachers of Mathematics, 1960).

of booklets entitled, *Exploring Mathematics on Your Own,* by Donovan A. Johnson and William H. Glenn. These booklets were prepared for use mainly in Grades 7 and 8; however, selected topics and exercises in several of the booklets would present an exciting challenge to some very capable fifth- and sixth-grade pupils. Topics such as "Understanding the Numeration System," "Fun with Mathematics," "Number Patterns," and "Short Cuts in Computing" are included in the series.

Projection Materials

Films, filmstrips, opaque and overhead projector materials, slides, and television kinescopes are classified as projection materials. Some school systems have a film library; others obtain films from film rental libraries such as those maintained by many colleges and universities. Most of the arithmetic films and filmstrips available are probably best used for summary and review purposes. Generally, more concrete experiences should precede the use of an arithmetic film or filmstrip. Arithmetic filmstrips may have some advantage over films because the rate of presentation can be governed and discussion can accompany the showing of a filmstrip.

A bulletin, *How to Use Films and Filmstrips in Mathematics,* is published by the National Council of Teachers of Mathematics. Information regarding available mathematics films and filmstrips may be found in *Educational Film Guide and Filmstrip Guide,* published by the H. W. Wilson Co., New York. Catalogs which give descriptions of films and filmstrip may be secured from producers of these materials. Some of the producers of educational films and filmstrips are: (1) Cornet Films, Chicago, Ill.; (2) Encyclopedia Britannica Films, Inc., Wilmette, Ill.; (3) Eye Gate House, Inc., Jamaica, N.Y.; (4) Johnson Hunt Arithmetic Productions, South Pasadena, Calif.; (5) Knowledge Builders, Visual Education Center Building, Floral Park, N.Y.; (6) Photo and Sound Productions, San Francisco, Calif.; (7) Popular Science Publishing Co., Audio-Visual Division, New York, N.Y.; (8) Teaching Films Custodians, Inc., New York, N.Y.; and (9) Young America Films, McGraw-Hill, New York, N.Y.

In addition to these producers, a recent series entitled *The New Elementary Mathematics Filmstrips,* for Grades 1–6, and directed by Bernard H. Gundlach, is produced by Colonial Films, Atlanta, Ga. Also, a recently available set of arithmetic enrichment filmstrips entitled *New Horizons in Arithmetic* and directed by Herbert F. Spitzer is published by Webster Publishing Company, St. Louis, Mo. A thorough compilation, description, and evaluation of arithmetic films and filmstrips available at the time of its publication may be consulted.[3]

The value of using an opaque projector or overhead projector to present enlarged illustrations for class study and discussion should not be overlooked. The teacher may collect pictures, select illustrations from supplementary books, and prepare charts, diagrams, and relationship tables for showing with an opaque projector. For showing with an overhead projector, illustrations may be drawn on transparencies with a grease pencil and aspects of the enlarged illustration may easily be pointed out and discussed. By tracing enlarged illustrations as these are projected on poster paper, arithmetic charts can be made. Television kinescopes will probably be more readily available in a few years. When such materials are carefully prepared, they help to enrich the arithmetic program for all learners; however, the teacher will still find it necessary to provide follow-up instruction and make allowances for individual needs. Television teaching cannot take the place of a classroom teacher who knows the interests and needs of the learner and can stimulate and observe pupil growth.

Community Resources

Community resources can be used effectively to develop an awareness of the important role of arithmetic in our society. Pupils can conduct interviews, invite speakers to the classroom, and take field trips.

Farmers, grocers, milkmen, postmen, department store clerks, policemen, weathermen, gas station attendants, engineers, accountants, and bankers are some of the people in the community who can be asked to explain their use of arithmetic with children. Pupils may also interview their parents as to how they use arithmetic and then

---

[3] Foster Grossnickle, Charlotte Junge, and William Metzner, "Instructional Materials for Teaching Arithmetic," *The Teaching of Arithmetic,* Fiftieth Yearbook, Part II, National Society for the Study of Education (Chicago: The University of Chicago Press, 1951).

share this information with the class. Drug stores, department stores, grocery stores, dairies, newspaper printing rooms, banks, post office shipping rooms, train depots, airports, building sites, and computer centers are a few of the places where pupils may observe arithmetic being used. Field trips taken into the community in relation to social studies or science units may also include a study of the importance of arithmetic in the social or scientific problems being studied. One source of suggestions regarding the use of community resources in the teaching of mathematics is, *Teaching Materials for Mathematics Classes,* Circular No. 399 (Washington, D.C.: U.S. Department of Health, Education, and Welfare, Office of Education).

CHAPTER V

Meeting Individual Differences

Individual differences which influence individual achievement are present in every classroom. Differences in interest and in ability to achieve in arithmetic exist among school children at every grade level. It is the teacher's responsibility to help each child achieve in accordance with his ability. In order to do this, the teacher must be able to determine factors causing differences in achievement and must know how to deal with these factors to develop the achievement potential of each child. This is a very difficult task which every teacher faces.

Factors Relating to
Achievement in Arithmetic

Any one factor or any combination of several factors may cause a pupil to differ from other pupils in arithmetic achievement. Studies indicate that high achievers in arithmetic display such personality and intellectual characteristics as a healthy ego, relative freedom from conflicts and anxieties, independent thinking, creativity, flexibility, and the ability to handle abstract symbols and relationships.[1] The following are commonly recognized factors relating to achievement in arithmetic:

1. *Intellectual ability.* Related to learning arithmetic are attentiveness; the ability to listen and follow directions; the ability to remember what is seen, heard, and read; the ability to express ideas clearly; and the ability to see relationships and to generalize. A pupil may not be able to perform well in one or several aspects of arithmetic because he is below average in general intelligence. Low intelligence, however, does not necessarily mean the child will do poorly in arithmetic: if he possesses certain other abilities, he may be able to overcome the handicap of a below-average intelligence. A pupil with higher intelligence, on the other hand, may be affected by

---

[1] Ernest A. Haggard, "Socialization, Personality, and Academic Achievement in Gifted Children," *The School Review,* 65 (1957), 388–414.

other factors in such a way that he is not achieving in accordance with his intellectual ability.

2. *Environmental influences.* Various environmental influences in the home, in the classroom, and in life outside of school may play a role in the pupil's achievement in arithmetic. Favorable environmental influences include a happy and stable home where parents and other members of the family have expressed enjoyment in learning arithmetic, experiences outside of school in which arithmetic plays an important role, and a classroom atmosphere which highlights arithmetic and helps to make its learning important and exciting.

3. *Emotional factors.* Emotional aspects can greatly influence learning. Favorable emotional factors include interest and appropriate attitude toward learning arithmetic, self-confidence, willingness to put forth effort to learn, pride in achievement, and systematic work habits.

4. *Physical factors.* Learning, like any other task, is best accomplished when the pupil eats proper foods, has sufficient energy, and feels generally well physically. Since seeing and hearing well are absolutely essential to learning, careful attention must be given to these factors and to the pupil's seating position in the classroom.

5. *Instructional factors.* Highly significant in regard to learning arithmetic are the instructional factors. Careful consideration should be given to such questions as: Has the pupil been helped to gain an understanding of the numeration system and the number operations? Has he mastered the basic facts of arithmetic introduced up to this point in his schooling? Has he been helped to understand and appreciate the social usefulness of arithmetic and to gain orderly ways of attacking quantitative problems? Has he been provided with sufficient practice on each new skill? Has he been challenged to explore and discover arithmetic? Have the content, methods, and materials used been adapted to meet his individual needs? Does the teacher enjoy arithmetic and have a good grasp of its basic principles?

When the teacher has identified factors which seem to be probable influences on the pupil's achievement in arithmetic, she must then take steps for dealing with these factors in such a way as to bring about the greatest achievement possible on the part of each pupil. Certain bad influences on achievement can be removed; others can be lessened. Certain other conditions cannot be changed but instruction can be adjusted so as to make allowance for them. In order to remove or lessen the effects of some bad influences on the child's arithmetic achievement, the services of others (parents, school nurse, or psychologist) may be required. In many cases, however, appropriate organization and instructional adjustments will suffice to meet individual differences.

There are many possible ways of varying class organization, arithmetic content, and learning activities; each teacher must select a combination of possibilities that fit and work together. There will also have to be schoolwide planning so that adjustments made in procedures for carrying out the arithmetic program fit together in such a way that each child moves smoothly and systematically through the total arithmetic program in the elementary school.[2]

Adjustments in Class Organization

Each of several types of class organization permits the teacher to make some provision for individual differences. Each teacher must select one or a combination of types of class organization which she can handle in terms of time and energy and in which the children whom she teaches seem to progress best. At this time there is not enough research evidence to afford any valid indications as to which of the various types or combinations of class organization may be most effective in providing for individual differences. Some of these types of organizations are:

1. *Whole-class organization.* In this type of organization, the teacher and heterogeneously grouped pupils move through the arithmetic program for the school year and the teacher gives help and encouragement to individuals as she recognizes the need and has the opportunity. All pupils are introduced at the same time to the basic list of topics taught in each grade and the whole class moves forward as a group through the topics usually considered by each grade. Efforts at meeting individual differences include help for individual pupils during the arithmetic period as much as time permits, occasional variations in practice, extra assignments for certain pupils, and whatever enrichment activities the teacher

---

[2] Casis School Faculty, *Meeting Individual Differences in Arithmetic* (directed and edited by Frances Flournoy and Henry J. Otto) (Austin, Texas: The University of Texas Press, 1959).

might encourage rapid learners to pursue individually. This type of class organization, if used alone, may not provide sufficient opportunity to differentiate content and to vary learning time, materials, and activities.

2. *Combination of whole-class and small-group organization.* The class is heterogeneously grouped and each new topic or topic for review is introduced to the class as a whole. The class is later divided in two or more groups so that the teacher may reteach where necessary, use varied materials, and provide differentiated assignments. When another new topic is to be introduced, the class again works as a whole. Individual differences are probably more systematically handled under this arrangement than the strict class-as-a-whole organization.

3. *Grouping within the class according to arithmetic achievement.* No effort is made to keep the entire class together as successive topics are studied. At the beginning of the school year, the class is divided into two or more subgroups on the basis of general arithmetic achievement. Each subgroup starts with the topics and level of difficulty at which it can experience reasonable success. Each group moves forward through the logical sequence of arithmetic topics at its own rate. The teacher divides her time among the groups as equitably as possible. There is considerable possibility in this type of arrangement for meeting the needs of the slow learner and for challenging the rapid learner.

4. *Completely individualized instruction.* Each pupil proceeds from one topic to another at his own rate. Each child would be using some self-teaching materials (workbook or textbook) appropriate for his level of achievement. Each child moves forward through this material at his own rate with minimum teacher guidance and with maximum self-direction in the developmental stages of a new topic as well as in the practice stages. This plan is limited by the great possibility that pupils would tend to perform on a mechanical level only, with no mathematical understanding or social appreciation. The motivation problem would be acute, especially for slow learners.

5. *Homogeneous ability grouping by whole classes.* In some schools in which this plan is used, the pupils in each grade are grouped according to general achievement in all areas of the school program. Although the pupils in each group are likely to be more generally alike in ability to learn, there will be some extremes in

this kind of an arrangement when one or more pupils in a class group of generally slow-moving pupils are average or above average in arithmetic ability or when one or more pupils in a generally fast-moving class are only average or below average in arithmetic achievement. Even in this kind of an arrangement some variations in content and teaching methods will be required to meet the needs of pupils who vary greatly from others in certain areas of the curriculum.

Other homogeneous whole-class grouping plans have involved grouping pupils of a certain grade according to levels of arithmetic achievement rather than levels of general achievement. If such a homogeneous whole-class grouping plan is used for another area, such as reading, pupils in the rapid-moving class of arithmetic pupils for the grade would not be exactly the same as those in the rapid-moving reading group. Pupils in the slow- and average-moving arithmetic groups would also differ some from these groups in the area of reading. Such an organization is very difficult to work out and to handle. Other variations of this organizational plan do now exist in some schools and have been tried in others.

Variations in Content

A procedure which seems to hold much promise in providing for individual differences affecting arithmetic achievement lies in varying the content.[3] Although there is a basic core of understandings and skills in arithmetic which all children should have in order to meet their mathematical needs now and in the future, the curriculum may often carry some children far beyond present and future needs for arithmetic to the point of frustration and at the same time may not sufficiently challenge and allow to go further those children who can and should do so. Some differentiation in content can and should be made in meeting the varying levels of ability to achieve and the varying needs and interests of children in the classroom.

For instance, rapid learners could be allowed to move through the usual array of topics more rapidly and use the extra time for

---

[3] J. Fred Weaver and Cleo F. Brawley, "Enriching the Elementary School Mathematics Program for More Capable Children," *Journal of Education,* 142 (October, 1959), 1–40.

more challenging or difficult topics. Infrequently used or difficult topics could be deleted from the curriculum of slower learners, and they could receive more help and practice in basic topics. In some schools, the additional topics for the rapid learners could be a horizontal type of enrichment and power-building content rather than topics to be taught in the next grade. Sources of such arithmetic activities have been presented in Chapter IV. Other schools might provide a vertical type of acceleration for the more rapid learner. In the vertical acceleration plan, rapid learners would be allowed to learn skills ordinarily taught in the next highest grade. For slower learners, some topics might be delayed until later in the grade or pushed up to the next grade. In this type of arrangement, the mathematics offering in junior high school would have to be articulated carefully with that of the elementary grades. Differentiated courses or differential treatment of pupils would have to prevail in junior high school so that all pupils might move forward from whatever points they had reached before leaving the elementary school. There is no evidence at present to prove which arrangement for selecting and spacing topics is more effective.

Variations in Instructional
Procedures and Materials

Adjustments in learning activities for meeting individual needs, interests, and levels of learning ability involve adjustments in teaching methods, materials, and learning time, as well as adjustments in content. Pupils on all levels of learning ability need a careful introduction to each basic arithmetic topic, the use of concrete and semi-concrete materials to aid in developing understanding, sufficient practice on each skill to be mastered, use of arithmetic in purposeful ways, systematic review to maintain skill and understanding, and systematic evaluation of progress. But the teaching methods and direct guidance required, the materials used, and the learning time allowed need to be varied for pupils on different levels of learning ability, interest, and achievement.

Instructional variations with rapid learners. Variations in teaching procedures and materials for fast learners might include (a) more independent reading and use of the textbook; (b) moving more rapidly from the use of concrete materials to the abstract level; (c) using extra challenge worksheets and chalkboard exercises from the teacher's manual and from other sources available to the teacher; (d) using frequent and more varied mental arithmetic shortcuts; (e) using a more difficult textbook, when available; (f) learning varied ways of checking; (g) participating in creative activities, such as creating interesting number patterns, planning mathematics quiz programs, making geometric designs, and writing plays about some phase of elementary mathematics; (h) reading supplementary books and pamphlets to gain greater insight into the nature and history of mathematics, to learn about additional topics of elementary mathematics, and to find out how mathematics is used in various vocations; (i) performing recreational arithmetic exercises; (j) having more difficult, challenging test items; and (k) conducting research on special topics—such as the principles of computers—by using encyclopedias, special pamphlets, and interviews. Though some challenges for fast learners could be offered during the regular arithmetic period after other basic program assignments have been completed, students might also be encouraged to work on special mathematics projects during other free time and after school.

Instructional variations with slow learners. Variations in teaching methods and materials for slow learners might include: (a) concrete experiences and materials to precede use of the textbook on a new topic; (b) very closely teacher-directed reading, study, and discussion of the textbook material; (c) longer and more frequent use of visual aids to supplement textbook pictures and exercises; (d) use of an easier textbook, when available; (e) oral reading of verbal problems by the teacher; (f) frequent dramatization of problem situations; (g) slower introduction of successive steps in a process; (h) mastery of only one simple way of checking computations; (i) more frequent reteaching of meanings and procedures; (j) frequent review; (k) shorter listening and practice periods; (l) more use of games to motivate learning; and (m) very short but frequent diagnostic tests.

CHAPTER VI

Evaluating Pupil Progress

Evaluation is a significant part of the total instructional program and should be a continuous process. Systematic evaluation indicates the extent to which goals are being achieved. As a result of using various evaluative procedures, steps can be taken to improve the instructional program in arithmetic and so to improve pupil learning of arithmetic.

Outcomes in Arithmetic Instruction

A knowledge of desirable arithmetic outcomes is essential in directing pupil learning. These outcomes serve as a guide in the evaluation of pupil learning as well as in the planning of instruction. The outcomes presented below should be viewed as being interrelated and interdependent, rather than separate and distinct.

Knowledge and understandings. A few studies of evaluation of pupils' understanding of arithmetic have been reported. In general, the results point to an inadequate understanding.[1] The learner's knowledge and understanding of mathematics should be extended at each grade level and generally relates to the following major concepts:

1. The idea of number;
2. The idea of one-to-one correspondence;
3. Principles of counting;
4. Characteristics of the base ten numeration system;
5. The meaning of the operations of addition, subtraction, multiplication, and division;
6. Relationships between specific number facts for the four number operations;
7. The commutative, associative, and distributive laws of arithmetic;
8. The meaning of computational algorisms;

---

[1] David Rappaport, "Understanding Meanings in Arithmetic," *The Arithmetic Teacher,* 5 (March, 1958), 96–99.

9. Relationships between common fractions, decimal fractions, and per cents;
10. Relationships of greater than, less than, and equality;
11. Arithmetic terms and symbols used to express quantitative ideas and relationships;
12. The idea of measurement and the relationship between common measures;
13. Principles of elementary geometry;
14. Uses of arithmetic in every day social affairs, in common occupations, and in selected business practices.

Attitudes and appreciations. The development of desirable attitudes and appreciations in arithmetic is also judged an important part of learning. Attitudes and appreciations regarding the following are important:

1. The vital role that mathematics plays in everyday life and in the advancements of mankind, such as scientific, industrial, and sociological advancements;
2. The efforts of men through the ages to develop an efficient number system and system of measurement;
3. The economy of time and effort which is characteristic of our numeration system and computational procedures;
4. A discovery attitude;
5. The importance of accuracy and suitable speed in performing arithmetical procedures;
6. The usefulness of rounding and estimation.

Skills. Arithmetic skills to be gained include:

1. Counting, reading, and writing numerals for whole numbers, common fractions, decimal fractions, and per cents;
2. Mastering basic number facts for addition, subtraction, multiplication, and division;
3. Computing with whole numbers, common fractions, decimal fractions, and per cents;
4. Solving simple equations, such as $15 \times n = 180$.
5. Using measuring devices and tables of measurement and finding perimeter, area, and volume;
6. Applying understandings and skills in solving real and stated word problems;
7. Rounding numbers and estimating answers;
8. Interpreting quantitative statements in terms of familiar reference measures;
9. Making simple mental computations;

10. Interpreting graphs, tables, and scale drawings, as well as arranging and presenting data in graphic or tabular form.

General growth. It is desirable that pupils should grow in the following general ways:

1. Developing intense interest in arithmetic;
2. Learning systematic listening and work habits;
3. Putting forth effort to learn in accordance with ability;
4. Using a variety of ways of solving examples and problems;
5. Giving explanations of ways of thinking in solving examples or equations and problems and supporting thinking with appropriate basic principles;
6. Developing self-confidence, resourcefulness, and initiative;
7. Exploring situations and making discoveries; inductive thinking;
8. Observing number patterns;
9. Noting relationships;
10. Generalizing;
11. Learning "if . . . then" or deductive thinking;
12. Using drawings and other visual materials to illustrate ideas;
13. Reading the textbook with understanding;
14. Verifying conclusions;
15. Locating computational errors and making corrections;
16. Recognizing problems and gathering related data for solving.

Purposes of Evaluation

Evaluation is an integral part of the total instructional program, and serves several important purposes. It is a means of checking on individual pupil growth and on the effectiveness of instructional procedures and materials. When pupils are not succeeding satisfactorily in the gaining of arithmetic understandings and skills and in developing problem-solving ability, steps should be taken to improve instruction.

Evaluation has motivational value, but the teacher must take care not to abuse this particular value derived from evaluation. However, having a knowledge of their progress does spur many learners on to better achievement in accordance with their ability to learn. Furthermore, evaluation serves as a guide for the teacher in (a) determining when learners are ready to proceed to the next step or topic; (b) recognizing if and what reteaching is needed; (c) identifying individual learning difficulties and seeking causes; (d) judging whether pupils are achieving in accordance with ability; and (e) judging appropriate and needed adjustments in learning activities, content, and materials to meet individual differences.

Systematic evaluation also provides evidence for reporting to parents on the learning progress of their children, and so plays an important role in parent-school relations. Evaluation reports become a part of each pupil's permanent record and are used to guide decisions on grade promotion and group placement and to formulate guidance and counseling programs.

Techniques for Evaluating

Thorough and continuous evaluation makes use of a variety of procedures for securing information about pupil progress. Various procedures for obtaining information about pupil learning in arithmetic include: informal teacher observation, textbook and teacher-made tests, standardized achievement tests, pupil folders, self-rating checklists, teacher-pupil conferences, and pupil summaries.[2]

Informal teacher observation. This technique is frequently used to: (1) note degree of attentiveness; (2) gauge pupil interest and attitude; (3) gain insight into the pupil's level and methods of thinking; (4) note evidence of maturity, or lack of it, in methods of work; (5) note evidence of understanding or lack of it; (6) locate faulty or incorrect procedures in written work; (7) determine whether pupils can apply arithmetic skills to solving quantitative problems which arise; (8) note ability to work with others; (9) note ability to do simple computation without using paper and pencil.

Although a great deal of valuable information may be gathered through alert teacher observation, it is difficult to remember everything observed, so some written records should be kept. An anecdotal record is an informal record kept on a pupil's general behavior, his actions and comments. Such records usually include only very significant things. The records may be kept in a small looseleaf notebook so that as many or as few pages as are needed may be inserted for any child. Such a record is of great value in conferences with the child, his parents, or his former teachers. A checklist of

---

2 William A. Brownell, "The Evaluation of Learning in Arithmetic," *Arithmetic in General Education,* Tenth Yearbook, The National Council of Teachers of Mathematics (Washington, D.C.: The Council, 1935).

things to look for may be prepared. The names of pupils might be listed in a vertical column, with terms across the top (such as "good," "satisfactory," or "unsatisfactory"). Such general items as attitude, attentiveness, initiative, effort, self-confidence, ability to generalize, and work habits might be included on one checklist. A second checklist might include items which indicate level of performance in understanding and skill on each arithmetic topic presented. Each topic could be included as needed: reading and writing numerals to 100, counting by 10's, counting by 5's, addition facts to sums of 10,"carrying" or regrouping, adding fractions with unlike denominators, dividing decimal fractions, and so on. Such checklists would furnish some evidence as to causes of learning difficulties and could serve as a basis for grouping children with common needs for reteaching.

Textbook and teacher-made tests. These materials are generally used to: (1) determine readiness for a new topic or new phases of a topic; (2) check pupil understanding of basic principles relating to the numeration system, number operations, measurement, and computational algorisms; (3) determine whether pupils have mastered the basic number facts; (4) check pupil mastery of computational procedures; (5) check pupil ability to estimate answers and do simple computation without paper and pencil; (6) check pupil ability to solve verbal problems; (7) identify learning difficulties and plan for reteaching; and (8) determine the extent of pupil's knowledge of arithmetical symbols and vocabulary.

Tests used in arithmetic are usually classified as "inventory" or "readiness," "achievement" or "progress," and "diagnostic." The inventory test is designed and generally used at the beginning of a school year to acquaint the teacher with each pupil's knowledge of those arithmetic understandings, skills, and vocabulary which he has been taught in earlier grades. However, many teachers prefer to give several shorter readiness tests throughout the school year to inventory the pupil's knowledge of concepts which are closely related to a new topic to be taught. When pupils are found to be lacking in certain concepts closely related to the new topic which is about to be taught, the teacher may plan to reteach or review certain areas before introducing the new topic.

A textbook or teacher-made achievement or progress test is generally used after an arithmetic topic or topics have been presented.

It should be designed to measure pupils' understanding of basic arithmetical principles, relationships, and vocabulary, as well as to measure computational skill and problem-solving ability. Through the achievement test, a teacher is able to determine the general level of a pupil's learning of the ideas included in the test and the pupil is kept aware of his learning progress.

A diagnostic test may be used to help identify the specific aspects of a topic on which reteaching or remedial work may be needed. Difficulties will vary from pupil to pupil. The nature of these difficulties should be identified and corrective measures taken. Diagnostic tests included in textbooks generally contain a sampling of examples relating to a single topic, such as subtraction of fractions. The examples are arranged from those involving simpler aspects of the topic to those involving difficult aspects. Frequently, five or six examples are of the same level of difficulty. If the pupil is found to be in error on two or more examples out of the five or six, he may need reteaching or further practice on this one element of the topic, depending on the nature of the errors. In providing remedial work, the teacher must begin at that level of the topic at which the pupil is succeeding and gradually proceed to more difficult levels. Though a diagnostic test will help to identify types of errors, it seldom reveals why a pupil is making a certain error. The teacher must rely on her observation of the pupil at work and on interviews with the pupil to find out how he is thinking, whether or not he understands procedures, and why he is having difficulties in learning.

Thorough consideration of the construction of arithmetic tests cannot be given here. Textbook and teacher-made tests are generally designed to check general knowledge, understanding, computational skill, vocabulary, and problem-solving ability. A variety of types of test items should be included. Common types of test items are computation exercises, fill-in or short-answer questions, multiple-choice questions, matching exercises, and true-false statements or yes-no questions.

Standardized achievement tests. A standardized achievement test is one on which the performance of an individual and the mean or median achievement of a single class may be compared to norms or standards (frequently expressed in the form of grade-equivalents) which have been established through large-scale experimental testing.

The content of a commercial standard test in arithmetic samples the arithmetic content of a series of grades. If a pupil in Grade 4 achieves a grade equivalent of 4.2 on a standardized arithmetic test taken in October, this means that the pupil has a grade achievement of fourth grade and two months, which would indicate that the pupil is achieving on his grade level. The fourth-grade pupil with a grade equivalent of 3.5 would be achieving below grade level. A grade level achievement of 5.0, or 6.2 would indicate that he is above average in arithmetic achievement.

The test items for standardized tests have been analyzed to identify and change or delete test items found, during trial testing, not to differentiate between good and poor achievers. The reliability of the test or the consistency with which it measures achievement has been determined. There are usually two or more equivalent forms for the same commercial standardized test. This means that the test items are not exactly the same on the two forms of the test, but that both forms are approximately equal in content, length, and reliability. Although standardized achievement tests in arithmetic do indicate how well a pupil or class is achieving in computation and problem-solving in comparison with normal expectations, most of the standardized tests now available are still quite inadequate for measuring understanding of arithmetic.

The result of standardized arithmetic achievement testing is generally used as an indication of the effectiveness of the arithmetic program. Such tests are also used to measure the degree of pupil progress in arithmetic over a period of a year or more. It should be understood, however, that the norms on supposedly comparable but different tests (as the California Test and the Metropolitan Test) are not equivalent. If the degree of pupil progress or class progress is to be considered then another form of the same test, rather than a different test series should be administered.

Publishers of standardized arithmetic achievement tests furnish sample test booklets and bulletins with information about the nature of the test, the content included, the forms available, and the cost. Descriptions and appraisals of such tests are available.[3] Some of the publishers of standardized arithmetic tests are:

---

[3] Oscar K. Buros, ed., *Mental Measurements Yearbook* (New Brunswick, N.J.: Gryphon Press, 1959).

California Test Bureau   Public School Publishing Company
Los Angeles, Calif.   Bloomington, Ill.

Educational Test Bureau   Science Research Associates
Minneapolis, Minn.   Chicago, Ill.

Educational Testing Service   World Book Company
Princeton, N.J.   Yonkers, N.Y.

Houghton Mifflin Company
Boston, Mass.

Individual pupil folders. The keeping of individual folders furnishes evidence for the teacher, the pupil, and his parents as to the pupil's level of achievement on each of the major topics of arithmetic studied during the school year. Two samples of a pupil's understanding and skill performance may be taken at different times of the year on such topics as are appropriate at a particular grade level. Samples of performance may be taken on such topics as counting; the numeration system; common fractions; decimal fractions; addition, subtraction, multiplication and division of whole numbers; common fractions, and decimal fractions; understanding and use of measures; understanding and determination of area and volume; knowledge of simple geometric shapes and principles; and verbal problems. The samples may be marked "excellent," "good," "satisfactory," or "unsatisfactory." When the second sample for a particular topic is placed in the folder, pupils may be guided by the teacher in comparing results and noting improvement. Samples should be stapled securely to the folders so that pupils may take folders home for parents to examine.

Arithmetic compositions. Pupils in the primary grades may write one or more simple sentences or draw pictures, and pupils in the intermediate grades may write paragraphs and also prepare illustrations about teacher-suggested arithmetic topics. Thus the pupil is encouraged to write about or to show his understanding of arithmetic topics and procedures. Some examples are: "What I Know About 6," "The Meaning of $\frac{1}{3}$," "How the Order of Counting 1 to 10 Helps Me Count by 10's to 100," "Ways I Use Fractions," "What Multiplication Means to Me," "What Dividing 48 by 4 Means," "The Many Names for $\frac{1}{4}$," "The Meaning of $6 \times 3\frac{1}{2}$," "The Meaning of Correctly Placing the Decimal in the Answer for $.6 \times 3.24$." The occasional use of such a technique gives the pupil an experience in learning to explain what he is thinking and gives the teacher another means of insight into a pupil's understanding. It should be remembered, however, that a pupil may have understandings about arithmetic but find it difficult to express such understanding in words. The use of this technique two or three times during a school year may help the pupil to learn gradually how to express his understandings of arithmetic.

Self-rating sheets. Individual self-rating sheets may be used as a means of teaching pupils to evaluate themselves and as a means of letting the teacher know how the child feels about himself regarding the learning of arithmetic. This procedure is probably most effective for Grades 3–6. The rating sheet might include the appropriate specific items such as interest, listening, discussion, work habits, neatness, effort to learn, reading the textbook, accuracy of work, finding own errors, knowing number facts (addition, subtraction, multiplication, and division), knowing computational procedures (with a list of appropriate skills for the grade level), and solving word problems. Columns for rating self as "good," "satisfactory," and "unsatisfactory" may be included. Such a rating sheet for arithmetic might be checked by the pupil twice during the year using different colors so that changes in self-rating might be noted.

Teacher-pupil conferences. This is generally recognized as an excellent means of exploring the pupil's interest in learning, helping the learner to evaluate his study habits, checking the pupil's thinking, and discovering causes of errors in written work. This procedure is of course very time-consuming. However, a few minutes spent in individual conference with the pupil as soon as some learning difficulty is noted may save a great deal of time, frustration, and discouragement later.

Bibliography

American Educational Research Association, *What Research Says to the Teacher: Teaching Arithmetic.* Washington, D.C.: The Association, 1963.

Banks, J. Houston, *Learning and Teaching Arithmetic.* Boston: Allyn and Bacon, Inc., 1959.

Bell, Clifford, Clela D. Hammond and Robert B. Herrera, *Fundamentals of Arithmetic for Teachers.* New York: John Wiley & Sons, Inc., 1962.

Buckingham, B. R., *Elementary Arithmetic: Its Meaning and Practice.* Boston: Houghton Mifflin Company, 1953.

Clark, John R. and Laura K. Eads, *Guiding Arithmetic Learning.* Yonkers-on-Hudson, N.Y.: World Book Co., 1954.

DeVault, M. Vere (ed.), *Improving Mathematics Programs.* Columbus, Ohio: Charles E. Merrill Books, Inc., 1961.

Dutton, Wilbur H. and L. J. Adams, *Arithmetic for Teachers.* Englewood Cliffs, N.J.: Prentice-Hall, Inc., 1961.

Encyclopedia of Educational Research. New York: The Macmillan Company (Arithmetic research reviewed), 1941, 1950 by Guy M. Wilson, 1960 by Guy T. Buswell.

Glennon, Vincent J. and C. W. Hunicutt, *What Does Research Say About Arithmetic?* Washington, D.C.: Association for Supervision and Curriculum Development, N.E.A., 1958.

Grossnickle, Foster E. and Leo J. Brueckner, *Discovering Meanings in Arithmetic.* Philadelphia: The John C. Winston Co., 1959.

Hollister, George E. and Agnes Gunderson, *Teaching Arithmetic in Grades I and II.* Boston: D.C. Heath & Company, 1954.

Marks, John L., C. Richard Purdy, and Lucien B. Kinney, *Teaching Arithmetic for Understanding.* New York: McGraw-Hill Book Company, Inc., 1958.

McSwain, E. T. and Ralph J. Cooke, *Understanding and Teaching Arithmetic in the Elementary School.* New York: Holt, Rinehart & Winston, Inc., 1958.

Morton, Robert L., *Teaching Children Arithmetic.* New York: Silver Burdett Company, 1953.

Mueller, Francis J., *Arithmetic, Its Structure and Concepts.* Englewood Cliffs, N.J.: Prentice-Hall, Inc., 1956.

National Council of Teachers of Mathematics, *The Teaching of Arithmetic,* Tenth Yearbook. Washington, D.C.: The Council, 1935.

———, *Arithmetic in General Education,* Sixteenth Yearbook. Washington, D.C.: The Council, 1941.

———, *The Growth of Mathematical Ideas: Grades K–12,* Twenty-fourth Yearbook. Washington, D.C.: The Council, 1959.

————, *Instruction in Arithmetic*, Twenty-fifth Yearbook. Washington, D.C.: The Council, 1960.

————, *Enrichment Mathematics for the Grades*, Twenty-Seventh Yearbook. Washington, D.C., The Council, 1963.

National Society for the Study of Education, *The Teaching of Arithmetic*, Fiftieth Yearbook, Part II. Chicago: University of Chicago Press, 1951.

Overman, James R., *The Teaching of Arithmetic*. Chicago: Lyons & Carnahan, 1961.

Peterson, John A. and Joseph Hashisaki, *Theory of Arithmetic*. New York: John Wiley & Sons, 1963.

Review of Educational Research. Washington, D.C.: American Educational Research Association, N.E.A. (Reviews of research on elementary school mathematics), October, 1931; April, 1934; December, 1937; October, 1940; October, 1942; October, 1945; October, 1957; June, 1961.

Schaaf, William L., *Basic Concepts of Elementary Mathematics*. New York: John Wiley & Sons, Inc., 1960.

School Mathematics Study Group, *Mathematics for the Elementary School Series: Teachers' Commentaries*. New Haven, Conn.: Yale University Press, 1960.

Spencer, Robert L. and Marguerite Brydegaard, *Building Mathematical Concepts in the Elementary School*. New York: Holt, Rinehart & Winston, Inc., 1952.

Spitzer, Herbert F., *Practical Classroom Procedures for Enriching Arithmetic*. St. Louis, Mo.: Webster Publishing Company, 1956.

————, *The Teaching of Arithmetic*. Boston: Houghton Mifflin Company, 1961.

Stern, Catherine, *Children Discover Arithmetic: An Introduction to Structural Arithmetic*. New York: Harper & Row, Publishers, 1949.

Stokes, C. Newton, *Teaching the Meanings of Arithmetic*. New York: Appleton-Century-Crofts, Inc., 1951.

Swain, Robert L., *Understanding Arithmetic*. New York: Holt, Rinehart & Winston, Inc., 1957.

The Arithmetic Teacher, Washington, D.C.: The National Council of Teachers of Mathematics, 1954 to present, published monthly.

Thorpe, Cleta B., *Teaching Elementary Arithmetic*. New York: Harper & Row, Publishers, 1962.

Wheat, Harry G., *How to Teach Arithmetic*. New York: Harper & Row, Publishers, 1951.

Index

Index

Date Due